BITEBACK RA...
67 DE...
LONDON...

Holy

Thom Braun is forty-some... ...ed with two children, and lives in Sur... ...n (of *The Good Life* fame). Born in Hackney in East London, he somehow found his way to St John's College, Oxford at the same time as Tony Blair. Not knowing what to do next, but deciding that the job of future Prime Minister was probably spoken for, he embarked on a strange and varied career. His first day at work was spent in the press gallery of the House of Commons, and from there he progressed through stages of writing books on Benjamin Disraeli, selling Persil, driving a pea harvester, and making TV commercials with Captain Birds Eye. Somewhere in the midst of all this he was ordained as an Anglican clergyman. He now splits his time between developing marketing solutions for very large companies, and working as a priest in a team ministry close to home.

Holy Orders

THOM BRAUN

Marshall Pickering
An Imprint of HarperCollinsPublishers

Marshall Pickering is an Imprint of
HarperCollins*Religious*
Part of HarperCollins*Publishers*
77-85 Fulham Palace Road, London W6 8JB

First published in Great Britain
in 1995 by Marshall Pickering

1 3 5 7 9 10 8 6 4 2

Text copyright © 1995 Thom Braun
Cartoons copyright © 1995 Paul Hampson

Thom Braun and Paul Hampson assert the moral right to be
identified as the author and illustrator of this work

A catalogue record for this book is
available from the British Library

ISBN 0 551 02 926-9

Printed and bound in Great Britain by
HarperCollinsManufacturing, Glasgow

CONDITIONS OF SALE

This book is sold subject to the condition that it
shall not, by way of trade or otherwise, be lent, re-sold,
hired out or otherwise circulated without the publisher's
prior consent in any form of binding or cover other
than that in which it is published and without a
similar condition including this condition being
imposed on the subsequent purchaser.

All rights reserved. No part of this publication may be
reproduced, stored in a retrieval system, or transmitted,
in any form or by any means, electronic, mechanical,
photocopying, recording or otherwise, without the prior
permission of the publishers.

For Jill

Contents

1 Not me, surely 1

2 Baptism of fire 18

3 Keeping Sunday special 38

4 A star is born 56

5 Meeting needs 75

6 Crossing over 96

7 Lent appeal 115

8 Pick 'n' mix 132

9 T.G.I.F. 150

10 Going under 168

11 Knock, knock, who's there? 187

Not me, surely

Then I heard the voice of the Lord saying,
'Whom shall I send, and who will go for us?'
(Isaiah 6:8).

WHEN I enter a church I normally seek out a place of quiet. A place where I can be alone for a few minutes. Alone to collect my thoughts, to talk to myself and to God. It is for this reason that my priority is usually to seek out the toilet.

Toilets, loos, lavatories — call them what you will — they all have an important place in my Christian pilgrimage. At times of crisis I have often found myself reassured by the privacy and peace of ecclesiastical comfort stations. Closeted within their various walls I have been able to find an uninterrupted peace, and the space in which to calm myself before christenings, weddings and funerals. They have given me precious private minutes to prepare for public celebrations and so have, in their way, taken on a special role in my spiritual development.

So it was that on a bright Sunday morning in October I found myself sitting in one of the most private places of Southwark Cathedral. I must have looked a sad picture, as I sat there fighting with a new and voluminous cassock. I could not be bothered to take it off completely, but found that hoisting it to my waist simply left me with a mass of unmanageable black material. Finally in despera

1

tion I threw the skirt up and over my head, so that it fell forward around my face like a big black cowl.

As the absurdity of the scene began to dawn on me, I started to experience a feeling of slight panic. What was clearly needed at this moment was an injection of calm reassurance. I unzipped the Bible I always carried with me and began to read the page where it had fallen open — at the prophet Isaiah.

'In the year that King Uzziah died, I saw the Lord sitting on a throne, high and lofty; and the hem of his robe filled the temple.'

Inside the dark and cavernous depths of my cassock I smiled to myself. If the Lord was able to deal with a robe that filled the temple whilst sitting on a high and lofty throne, I should (I felt) be able to manage an unfamiliar cassock whilst perching on a rather lower seat. Filled with a new feeling of confidence and purpose I sat back to consider my position.

Here I was, sitting in splendid isolation and preparing for what was likely to be one of the most important events of my life. Today was the day of my ordination. The day when I would be ordained as a church minister. I pushed my hand through the folds of cassock that were draped around my face and felt, once again, the new dog collar encircling my neck. This time my smile erupted into an audible laugh. What on earth had happened to me? I used to be normal, I reflected. I used to spend my Sundays lying in bed, enjoying a late lunch of roast beef, and watching football on the TV.

But all that had changed. It had begun to change when I first received my calling, my 'Holy Orders' as I had decided to call it. It was then that I had embarked on the road that was to lead through three years of theological training. A road which had now brought me to the point where those Holy Orders would be formalized and made public. A road which, in the days and weeks to come, would lead who knew where. A true calling it may have been, but there was a bit of me that still did not understand 'why', and was beginning to worry about 'how'. A bit of me that was as ready as ever to say, 'Not me, surely'.

As always, however, there came the point where the rationalization and the denial had to stop. It was usually at that point that faith, in all its glorious imprecision, would force me to embrace the irrational and get stuck in. I glanced at my watch and realized it was time to get moving. I wrestled myself back into a full length of cassock, washed my hands, took a deep breath and made a determined move into the high space of the crowded cathedral that was, by now, humming with anticipation.

Back in the relative privacy of the retro-choir behind the high altar, the other men and women who were to be ordained with me were beginning to put on their surplices in readiness for the opening procession. I did likewise, and then sat down once more to try to gather my thoughts. It was still only a quarter to eleven in the morning, and yet it had already been an extraordinary day.

* * *

The alarm on my wristwatch had woken me at six o'clock, and I lay for a few minutes staring up at the ceiling of the room in which I had slept for the last three nights. When you are about to be ordained you are sent to a retreat house for a few days, away from friends and family, until the morning of the ordination when you emerge once again onto the

3

stage of the world to become one of those strange beings — a clergy person.

Those few days away provide a time to reflect on what has brought you to this point and on what lies ahead. It is a time mainly of silence and prayer. A time which, depending on your state of mind, can be either very relaxing or very fraught.

I had found it very much a pleasure. Whilst it meant time away from my wife Cheryl and my daughter Amy, it was also an opportunity to unwind from my job at the advertising agency. I had left the office on Wednesday night with my head whirling from a long and acrimonious meeting. The creative director had used his very colourful language in castigating one of our most prestigious clients, who had had the temerity to criticize the agency's advertising for the new washing liquid, 'Macro-Suds'. It would presumably be up to me to retrieve the situation during the following week. In the meantime, I could only hope that things would not deteriorate in my absence.

At a personal level, my time at the retreat house would be yet another opportunity to reflect on the relationship between the world of work and a calling within the church — for I could already see only too clearly that keeping the two in balance was going to provide me with some notable challenges.

When I had first experienced what I felt as a calling some four or five years before, I had considered the possibility of doing it full-time — that is, giving up my job in order to train full-time, and then making the church my sole vocation, becoming in due course a full-time parish priest. Soon afterwards, however, I learned for the first time about the existence of MSEs — Ministers in

Secular Employment. Clergy who usually trained on a part-time basis, and who kept their secular jobs as a way of earning a living.

The whole idea of becoming a church minister, whilst remaining at the same time an account director in a major London advertising agency, immediately attracted me. On the one hand there was the opportunity of being able to do *both* the jobs that most appealed to me. On a slightly less selfish note perhaps, I started to consider the very real possibilities for developing a new sense of Christian mission — one which was forced to interpret in a theological sense the weird and wonderful world of marketing and advertising as much as it did the perennial vagaries of life in a parish.

And so it was that, with the full support of my wife Cheryl, and the backing of the local church where we worshipped, I embarked on three years of part-time theological study which was meant to prepare me for the dual life of being both an advertising man and a clerk in holy orders.

During those three years Amy had grown from being a toddler into a confident schoolgirl, and Cheryl had resumed her career as a college lecturer. They were three years which, for many reasons, had been full of laughter and tears. But that's another story.

The important thing was that those years, and the support of those who were close to me, had brought me to this point. The point from which I was about to embark on a new road of Christian ministry — for better, for worse; for richer, for poorer. It was, after all, a bit like getting married all over again — although I sometimes think Cheryl was more inclined to see the Church as my mistress.

Many of those thoughts crowded into my mind as I lay staring up at the ceiling on that Sunday morning in October, the day of the ordination. A generous feeling of spirituality and goodwill radiated from every inch of my body, as I lay soaking up the peace and tranquillity of the new day. That feeling, however, was quickly destroyed by the sound of the morning bell being vigorously rung outside my room by the designated monitor for the day. I leaped to my feet and opened the door with a hearty greeting.

'Shut that wretched noise, for goodness sake! Some of us are trying to pray, you know!'

Ken at first seemed taken aback by my salutation, but he then started waffling on about how bells had always been more of a call to prayer than a disruption of it, from the very earliest times in England. I responded with a curt phrase to the effect that I considered it unlikely that there had *ever* been any times earlier than this.

He retreated with a hurt and gloomy expression on his face. That, in itself, was somewhat unusual. Ken had a plump open face, very short brown hair, and large owlish glasses which seemed always to be halfway down his wide and shapeless nose. It was strange not to see the usual smile on his face. The smile which seemed to inhabit only the lower reaches of his face. His small eyes would stare back at you in a particularly earnest way whenever you spoke to him, but the mouth was nearly always curled up into something of a smile. Ken had, I believe, discovered about ten years before that Jesus loved him, and felt it incumbent on him to express a feeling of inner joy by displaying his teeth to all and sundry on an almost permanent basis.

6

Ken was very loveable, but I have to admit that his smile often had the same effect on me as a red rag to a bull. I felt duty bound to undermine it whenever I could. It wasn't that I didn't like Ken. I did, in a funny sort of way. And I was sure that Jesus liked him too. Ahead of Ken, I felt sure, lay a life of difficult and painful ministry. Somehow I knew that I could see that reality much more than Ken could himself.

Ken was never happier than when he was singing with his guitar or poring over the pages of a Bible that had been almost worn through by the attentions of his highlighter pens. What worried me, however, was the unworldly innocence that Ken radiated. That's not, I hope, to be too cynical, nor to suggest that my own way of life was somehow a model of Christian living. It certainly wasn't. My fear was simply that Ken's faith in the inherent meekness of people would ill prepare him for the world that I saw shuffling past my West End window every day.

Ken probably had similar misgivings about me. Sometimes I thought of him spending the whole of the three years of training convinced that I was only on the course because of a clerical error. In one idle moment, I had imagined him phoning to check up on me.

'Hello, this is Kenneth Slemen. I'm ringing about a colleague of mine, Michael Dunn. Yes, D.U.N.N. He's training with me on SLOP. Yes, the South London Ordination Programme. I'm just wondering if you could confirm one thing about him for me. Is he actually a Christian? Why do I ask? Well, it's just that he is — how can I put it? — rather *worldly* in his ways.'

Poor Ken! We got on all right really, but I couldn't resist baiting him when I had the chance. He seemed to have the notion that being a Christian — and certainly being a clergy person — was all about being weak, humble and unassuming, and that somehow this approach to life was Christ-like.

From my point of view he could not have been more wrong. Do you really think, I used to say to him, that the Jewish and Roman authorities would have clubbed together to assassinate a man they saw as weak, humble and unassuming? Jesus Christ was bumped off because he was trouble. He was a pain in the backside, and a very disruptive influence.

Forget all this talk about Jesus being the fulfilment of what had been prophesied, I used to tell him. Jesus didn't fit in with *anybody's* pattern. He was difficult, sharp, angular, awkward to deal with, and generally downright provocative. He wasn't what anyone expected him to be. He said things and did things that got up people's noses. *That's* why he was killed. Because he *disturbed* people. Because he was a troublemaker, and because he challenged people to reappraise the whole question of God, the world, and the meaning of life.

It was at this point that Ken used to reinforce his smile and start quoting bits of Scripture at me, like 'Blessed are the meek'. My response (I couldn't stop myself) was usually to say something like 'You can't take Bible texts out of context' — which used to send him away shaking his head and threatening to pray for me.

I leaned forward and blinked into the mirror at three days of stubble on my chin. Ah well, I mused, in a few hours' time Ken and I would be going out into the world as fellow clergymen, probably to speak and act in very different ways — except for the fact that our words and our deeds would all be said and done in the name of the same Jesus Christ.

As it turned out, what Ken said and did was probably the more valuable. When I met him again by chance a few years later, I realized that I had only been half-right in my analysis of how he would fare. All of which taught me something more about what it means to serve. On that ordination morning, however, all of that was still a long way in the future.

Having seen off Ken, it was time for a shower and a shave. Soon I was ready to dress, conscious of the fact that we were all expected at this point to put on our dog collars for the first time. I had toyed with the idea of looking conventionally clerical for the day of the ordination, and had invested in a couple of traditional black shirts. When it came to the crunch, however, and I was packing my suitcase on the Wednesday night, I decided that they weren't really me.

Some months earlier I had discovered a certain Mrs Hinckley who lived just outside Oxford and who was happy to make customized clerical shirts for a select number of personal clients. After a very pleasant afternoon tea with her one day during the summer, she had agreed to make three shirts for me — one in yellow, one in blue and red stripes, and one in black with white polka dots. It was this last one which I had brought with me to the retreat house, resolved to wear it with my pink Hugo Boss linen jacket and my black Paul Smith trousers.

Perhaps because I am not very tall, I have always been very conscious of making sure that my clothes fitted me well, and this particular combination (with the exception of the shirt, of course) was a favourite blend of comfort and fashion. I stared into the mirror once again, pushing my fingers through what remained of my curly blond hair, and decided that I was ready to face the world.

The programme for the day began with prayers in the retreat house chapel. This would be the first opportunity for my colleagues and me to see each other in our clerical dress. There had been fifteen of us doing the course together, and ten (including myself) were to be ordained as deacons on this Sunday morning. Of the ten, four were men and six women and, as I entered the chapel, I noticed that most were already there, sitting in a semi-circle in front of the altar. Everyone seemed to be in some state of prayer or meditation, except the principal, Dr Soley, who was looking at my shirt as if it were somehow a sign of devil worship.

He must have been sending out vibrations of some kind, because within a few seconds everyone looked up or opened their eyes to review the said item of clothing. Some faces (like the one of Brian Lovett, a straight-talking Falstaffian man who was a coach driver by trade) appeared to radiate amused approval. Others (like Ken) stared in disbelief. I didn't mind. In fact, I rather enjoyed it. And, as I closed my eyes to thank the Lord for the majesty of another day, I felt sure that God would not be dividing the sheep from the goats on the basis of their shirts.

The retreat house was in a rural part of Surrey and, once breakfast was over, it was time to drive to the cathedral at Southwark. I had my car with me and so offered the available spare seats to those who had arrived on public transport. Ken said thank you, but he had already been offered a seat by Rosemary, a cuddly teacher from Epsom. Brian said yes, and so did Rita, a large and strong-willed sculptress from Croydon.

The three of us set off almost at once, with Rita claiming confidently that she knew a smart short cut through south London.

Why do I always believe confident people when they say they know something? I suddenly realized that I had spent most of the last three years implicitly believing what Rita said because she always sounded so convincing and unswerving. I never thought to question anything that came from her lips. It was about forty minutes later, however, that I began to have my doubts when we found ourselves in the middle of an industrial estate, with Brian scrabbling around under the seats for the old London Road Atlas that I thought must be somewhere in the car.

'They've obviously changed it all since I last came this way,' said Rita in a way that laid the blame clearly at the feet of some unidentified local municipal body.

'Yes,' I agreed wanly. Who was I to gainsay Rita? For all I knew, she was right. Perhaps they (whoever 'they' were) *had* changed the roads. But somehow there was that nagging doubt that it was Rita who was wrong. I couldn't get cross with her. In many ways I admired her. I rather wished that I could be as certain of anything as Rita was of everything.

'Found it,' said Brian suddenly, wrenching a tattered paperback from the murky depths beneath the passenger seat and passing it to me.

'The abridged *Around the World in Eighty Days*,' I said dryly, throwing it back at him. 'Well, that should certainly help.'

There was nothing for it, I thought. All we knew was the name of the road we were in, and there was a distinct danger that we could be driving around for another half-hour without finding our way. I was going to have to disturb Cheryl.

'Morning, darling,' I crooned into the car-phone, quickly adding, 'Don't say anything rude because I've got two card-carrying Christians with me and they might be shocked.' Fortunately Cheryl was able to find a street map of London and tell us where we were — which was nowhere near where we were supposed to be.

What happened over the next few minutes resembled something like those airline disaster movies, where the double-glazing salesman takes the controls of the aircraft after the pilot has passed out, and is talked down onto the runway by the experienced but intemperate veteran in the control tower.

Brian took the phone from me as I started to drive again. He relayed the instructions as Cheryl talked us out of the labyrinthine industrial estate by giving us directions as we went along. In about ten minutes we were back on to some vaguely recognizable roads with the street signs reassuring us that we were heading in roughly the right direction.

'We should be OK now, darling,' I said into the phone as confidently as I could. 'You and Amy had better get moving. Take care, and I'll see you at the cathedral.'

I looked at my watch. We were behind schedule as far as I could see, and would need to speed up if we were to get there with time to spare.

'Right, you two, hang on!'

One of the good things about Sunday mornings is that the roads are usually not too busy. The enormous growth in car-boot sales and Sunday trading has meant that a lot more people venture out and about than was ever the case a few years ago. But, even so, it is still relatively quiet in large parts of the city, and so I found I had an almost clear road ahead of me. Unfortunately it was not the road *ahead* that was the problem.

When I saw the blue flashing light in my rear-view mirror I immediately slowed down, pulled up by a bus-stop and told Brian and Rita to leave the talking to me. I was concerned that, between them, Brian's homely coach-driving wisdom and Rita's forthright advice might land us in more trouble than we were clearly in already.

I lowered the window to find myself looking up at a stout police officer who was obviously determined to avoid eye contact with a member of the criminal classes. He stared resolutely at the top of the car as he made his opening greeting in a dull flat tone.

'Do you know what speed you were travelling at, sir?'

'I'm afraid not, officer,' I said truthfully, although I suspected that it had been about sixty miles an hour.

'And do you know what the speed limit is here, sir?'

'I'm afraid not, officer,' I said, again truthfully.

The officer looked down at me for the first time and paused momentarily as he saw the collar.

'This is a thirty mile an hour area, sir, and you were travelling well in excess of that speed.'

I looked suitably penitent and managed to stop myself from saying, 'It's a fair cop'. Instead, I coughed, trying to think of how I could explain why we were in a hurry without getting tied up in the details of training, ordination and the meaning of life.

'Look, I'm terribly sorry, officer, but I and my fellow . . . that is my fellow . . . my fellow *vicars* are on our way to a big service at the cathedral, and . . . Well, if we don't get there on time . . . Well, it's almost a matter of life and death . . . Well, not literally, you understand. That is, no one will *die* exactly. But it will be a bit of a — well, you know — a bit of a letdown, and all that. And I think the bishop will be a bit cross. And Aunty May's coming all the way from Chester . . .'

My words drifted away into an incoherent gurgle. Brian and Rita were staying resolutely mute as briefed, although I could hear them both breathing noisily and shifting in their seats.

'And so you're a vicar are you, sir,' said the policeman in a voice that seemed to carry a hint of weary sarcasm and possibly menace as he focused on the white polka dots of my shirt. 'And this, er, this lady here. She's a vicar as well, is she, sir?'

'Well, not exactly *vicars* as such, officer,' I said, feeling the ground opening up under me.

'Not *as such*, sir?' said the policeman. 'Not *exactly* vicars, did you say, sir?'

'Not exactly. No, officer,' I said, attempting a smile.

'Indeed, sir. Indeed,' he said, crossing his arms, and once more looking at the car. 'Because I have to say, sir, that in eight years in the force I have not come across a vicar with a spotty shirt, sir. Nor a lady vicar, sir. Nor, in fact, a vicar driving a rather large BMW, sir.'

'Ah yes,' I croaked feverishly. 'It must all look a bit odd.'

The policeman sucked his teeth loudly before saying:

'Just a bit, sir. Just a bit.'

As fate would have it, at just that moment an old green Morris Minor passed us at a sedate speed and stopped a few yards ahead. The doors opened and out got Ken and Rosemary.

The police officer turned in their direction to see two more dog collars coming towards him with ingratiating smiles and a great show of teeth.

'Oh God,' I think I heard him mutter. 'Why me?'

From that moment, however, things seemed to improve. Thanks to the testimonies of Ken and Rosemary, the policeman decided to let me off with a warning. We then set off in convoy, with Rosemary and Ken leading the way and me following on at a speed more appropriate for a funeral cortege. How we ever arrived at the cathedral on time I will never know, but arrive we did.

My watch said that it was a quarter past ten in the morning, although I felt ready for my first gin and tonic of the day. Such a beverage, however, not being available in the cathedral, I was grateful to accept a cup of Rosemary's sweet coffee which she poured from the biggest Thermos flask I have ever seen.

As I sat down in a quiet corner I realized for the first time that I was shaking slightly. I stared up at one of the stained-glass windows and tried to calm myself with a prayer.

This is it, I thought. This is really it. And here am I.

* * *

As we processed in, to the strains of 'Christ is made the sure foundation', I felt the hairs stand up on the back of my neck. It was like floating. Almost never had I experienced a perambulation like it, as we made our way around the cathedral and up the centre aisle to our places on either side of the bishop's throne.

The service was a delight from beginning to end, and I could see the joy radiating from each of my colleagues as they were swept up and carried along by the occasion. Ken, Brian, Rita, Rosemary, and the others. Their faces all shone with a light I had only ever glimpsed before. The reality of the experience was completely different to what I had imagined, and when the bishop placed his hands on my head I felt awash with the beauty of the moment.

16

'Send down the Holy Spirit upon your servant Michael for the office and work of a deacon in your Church.'
Those were the words he said to each of us individually, and in those words we bathed, aware at the same time of our impoverishment and our great good fortune.

At that moment I felt overwhelmed by the simplicity, the beauty, the mystery and the wonder of the Christian faith. How was I ever going to find words to explain it to others? To reduce it to a set of simple dogmas or rallying calls would be to miss its essential wonder — that God loves us in spite of what we sometimes say and do in his name. It was a moment that would stay with me for the rest of my life.

When I emerged into the bright sunshine to the kisses and hugs of Cheryl, Amy and a host of friends and relatives, I was different from how I was when I entered the cathedral. No, I had not changed physically or mentally. I am not sure even that my spirit had been changed. But something had happened that could not be undone.

A life in Holy Orders lay open before me, and it was now my responsibility to make the best of it one way or another.

TWO

Baptism of fire

After the earthquake a fire, but the Lord
was not in the fire; and after the fire a
sound of sheer silence. (1 Kings 19:12)

'IT WAS out of this world,' I said in reply to Janie's
question about the ordination. I was, after all,
now back in the world of advertising.

'Really!' she said, with a face that showed sympathy and support, but also betrayed her
complete incomprehension. 'Did the earth
move?'

We both laughed, bundled together our files
and made our way to meeting room three.
Another Monday morning at work. It wasn't long
before my feet were well and truly back on the
ground.

'For crying out loud!' said Chris Mulligan,
Marketing Manager of Pronto Pizzas, in his best
lip-curling manner.

I stared back at him, trying to look conciliatory.

'Do you *want* this business or not?' Mulligan
continued, obviously liking the sound of his own
voice. 'Because if you *don't*, there are plenty more
agencies out there who'd be hungry for it!'

I sometimes wonder how effective those
'arrow prayers' are. You know, the thoughts you
shoot up to God in less time than it would take to
say a single word. I must have let a couple go
winging on their way before opening my mouth

to respond, although I can't honestly say now whether they were requests for strength, patience, diplomacy, safety, or simply a plea for the ability to tell Mulligan just where he could stick his frozen pizzas.

'May I say something?' I said at last, trying to assume a tone of calm.

Mulligan leaned back heavily in the chair and threw his pencil onto the table. I decided that this meant 'yes'.

'Well, first of all, Chris,' I continued, with an attempt at creating a mood of friendship, 'I have to say that the brief did not *specify* that the new work had to be for posters or print. Pronto Pizzas have always been advertised on television before.'

'Michael, Michael,' growled Mulligan, winding up again for an assault. 'I know how my own brand has been advertised, thank you all the same. I pay you guys to come up with the future, not to tell me the past.'

I could tell he was pleased with this remark. It seemed to make him feel that he was cleverer than the two of us, and so he was able to relax slightly. I decided to press on.

'The fact is, Chris, we would be *delighted* to look at ways of making the creative idea for Prontos work well in print and posters. It's just that the brief did not specify, and we – quite naturally, I think – followed the logical TV option.'

Mulligan was beginning to think about lunch. There was a certain mellowness creeping into his expression. He sighed the sigh of a weary businessman, confronted by those otherworldy beings from the advertising agency, who (of course) would not recognize a real business problem if it came up and hit them in the face.

'Look, Michael, I'm a busy guy. I've got lots of fish to fry.'

He smiled that inane smile of his. Oh, give me strength, I thought – now he thinks he's a poet.

'And those fish aren't going cheap, Michael.'

I prayed that Janie would not make the obvious remark about it being budgies, and not fish, that go cheep.

Mulligan was warming to his theme.

'I've got budgets to manage, Michael . . .'

That's a relief, I thought. Budgets, not budgies. I fought to keep the smile off my face.

'. . . and there's no way that those budgets can stretch to swallowing your TV just to cover an "even more pepperoni" slug.'

He certainly had a way with words.

'Right, Chris, point taken,' I said, beginning to shuffle my papers on the table. 'Let's talk about a revised timing plan over a glass of wine and a spot of lunch, shall we?'

Mulligan gave the mandatory pained look, sucked his teeth, and studied his watch, before appearing to do us a great favour by agreeing to the suggestion.

'Well, just a quick one then. I can't afford to be away for too long, you know. Although this thing,' he said, patting his mobile phone affectionately, 'makes life a bit more bearable. And the guys back at the ranch know they're never out of my shouting range.'

Janie and I politely joined in his laughter and I wondered what it might have been in Mulligan's past that made his conduct betray such insecurity.

Meeting room three was one of the agency's

larger conference rooms, and lunch was wheeled in on a trolley at the far end. Janie poured Mulligan a glass of wine, and the client began to be predictably expansive and filled with grotesque bonhomie.

'Look, I know you guys are good guys really. I trust you to come up with the goods. And, OK, the brief didn't *say* print and posters. But, come on!'

He shrugged, and I tried to look as if I knew what I was supposed to be 'coming on' about.

'OK,' he continued, 'perhaps I was a bit hard on you guys. But I do want that print and poster stuff – and I don't want you to give me any of that "it'll take four weeks" nonsense. I want it in two weeks, OK?'

'OK,' I echoed. 'Two weeks, Chris. We'll rebrief the creative team straight after lunch.'

'Good stuff, Michael.' Mulligan made his comment with a leer in Janie's direction, before adding, 'and I don't just mean the Chardonnay!'

I assumed my 'oh, you're such a wag' look, while I could see that past Mulligan's shoulder, and out of his range of vision, Janie was feigning being sick in the ice bucket.

The client took a large swig from the glass, and adopted something of a matey and confidential air.

'Now what's all this stuff about you being a vicar, Michael?'

Ah, at last, I thought. We're off the subject of Pronto Pizzas.

'Not a vicar exactly, Chris. More a deacon, in fact.'

'And what's a *deacon* when he's at home?'

'Well, in a way it's a bit like being a trainee priest.'

'Which is the same as being a vicar.'

Mulligan made it sound like a definitive statement rather than a question.

'Not necessarily. After a year as a deacon I will be ordained a second time as a priest – which means I will be able to do all the various things you normally associate with clergy. Things like presiding at the Eucharist or the Lord's Supper.'

'The bread and wine bit, you mean.' Again, Mulligan's tone of voice might have suggested that he was explaining it all to me, rather than the other way round.

'Yes. But because I have another job as well, working here for the agency, the church doesn't pay me, and I spend only part of my week actually being a clergyman in my home parish.'

'But when you *are* there, then you're the vicar, right?'

'Not quite, I'm afraid. The vicar is the person who lives and works in the parish all the time, and who is responsible for what goes on there. We have two churches in our parish, and we also have a second full-time clergyman who helps the vicar keep the whole show on the road, as it were. I'm now the third and last member of the clergy team in that parish, and so I will be trying to do as much as I can whilst still earning a living here – by developing the new advertising for Pronto Pizzas, among other things.'

Mulligan was beginning to get restless, although some of the most obvious symptoms disappeared when Janie refilled his glass.

'So you're a part-time priest or deacon, or whatever it is you are,' he said with self-proclaimed authority.

'I don't see it as part-time,' I said, smiling broadly. 'I'm a Christian and a minister *all* the time. It's not something you can switch on and off like a light

22

bulb. It just so happens that sometimes my sphere of ministry is in the parish where I live, and sometimes it's in the world where I work for a crust. I'm a clergyman all the time, Chris – even while I'm speaking to you now.'

'You are? Christ! I mean . . . Really?'

Mulligan looked perplexed. As if his position of assumed superiority might be in danger of slipping from him. He looked away from me, transferring his gaze unsubtly to Janie's chest as she leaned across the table with a large plate of sandwiches.

'You must tell me about it sometime,' he said in a shallow and soothing way which I knew meant that his thoughts were engaged elsewhere.

Just don't tell me about it *now*, was what he really meant. So I took the hint and steered the conversation back onto the sort of subjects he was likely to be more comfortable with.

It would not be appropriate, I reflected, to try to push a conversation on the subject of my calling. That whole area was something that would have to be left to grow over time. God willing, there would be opportunities in the coming months for me to meet *that* particular brief.

* * *

St Mary's 'Parish Surgery' was held on Monday evenings between seven and eight o'clock, and I decided to look in on my way home. I managed to leave the agency soon after half past six, and arrived at St Mary's at a quarter past seven.

'Parish Surgery' is the name given to the hour in the week when parishioners can drop in without an appointment to arrange church matters with the clergy or the verger. Most of the time tends to be taken up with bookings for weddings and baptisms, but occasionally it acts as a focus for other concerns. I let myself in by the side door and went straight to the parish office, where Colin the verger was in conversation with a man and a woman.

Colin Grey was a long stick of a man, of indeterminate age, with a thin reedy voice that seemed purpose-built for delivering the dry facts of banns and special marriage licences. Colin had grown up in North London under the guidance of a devout Catholic nanny. Our parish of St Mary's and St John's was pretty much middle-of-the-road when it came to church tradition, although the vicar was encouraging the congregation to try different types of services. Within the very wide spectrum of personal tastes, styles and beliefs in the parish, Colin very much represented the High Church party. He was never seen in church without a black cassock, and always made a point of calling all the clergy 'Father'.

'Ah,' he crooned, the merest hint of a death rattle adding some macabre interest to his already strained tone. 'Father Michael.'

I pulled a face, but quickly had to turn my grimace into a smile for the benefit of the couple who sat across the desk from him. I had spent several years trying to come to terms with the fact of my impending ordination, but little more than twenty-four hours after the deed itself I wasn't at all sure that I liked the idea of being called 'Father'.

My feeling of awkwardness was made even more pronounced by the expressions of the man and woman. They both turned to face me, probably expecting to see a sensible-looking person in a black suit or cassock. Instead they saw a somewhat embarrassed chap in an ultramarine linen suit and a bright floral tie.

I held out my hand.

'I, er, that is, the Reverend Michael Dunn, at your service,' I said unconvincingly. They both nodded as if to say, 'If you say so'.

'Mr and Mrs Kent have come to arrange the baptism of their son, William,' said Colin.

'Right,' I said sagely, pulling up a chair.

'And I have indicated,' continued Colin, 'that you would probably be the one to do it.'

'The arranging, you mean?' I said.

'No. The baptism itself.'

'Right,' I said. 'Of course.'

Needless to say, I had not performed a baptism before, and I wasn't sure whether this was the moment to come clean, as it were, with Mr and Mrs Kent. I needn't have worried, for Colin took the decision out of my hands.

'Father Michael,' he said, putting the ends of his long fingers together in a confidential manner, 'is very newly ordained, and this will be his first baptism.'

Mr and Mrs Kent turned their wan faces back towards me. They were clearly not over-impressed by the prospect of having their infant baptized by a 'very newly ordained' minister. In fact, they looked much as I imagine people might look if you told them that their car was going to be 'fixed' by the most recently recruited trainee mechanic, or that their fillings were going to be drilled by a newly qualified dentist.

I felt it was time to show that I knew something of the procedures at St Mary's.

'And which Sunday afternoon are we talking

about here, Colin?' I said, reaching for my diary.

'Sunday *morning*, Father. It will be a Sunday morning. Mr and Mrs Kent would like the baptism to take place within the normal Sunday morning service. So you'll have quite an audience!'

His laugh resembled the sound of a car trying to start on a cold morning.

I thought, 'Oh, dear', but said 'Jolly good', in a falsely bright tone.

Mrs Kent leaned forward to speak.

'We're not regular churchgoers,' she said.

'Christmas and Easter, really,' added Mr Kent.

'And Mother's Day,' said Mrs Kent.

'Not forgetting Harvest Festival,' added Mr Kent.

'Indeed not,' I said. 'Who'd want to forget Harvest Festival? And how old is little .. ?'

'William,' said Colin.

'Yes. William,' I said. 'How old is William?'

Mr Kent smiled the smile of a proud father.

'Five,' he said.

'Five months,' I said. It wasn't a question. More a statement.

'Oh, *no*,' said Mrs Kent. There was a small burst of laughter from both the Kents, punctuated by various rattling noises from Colin.

'William is five *years* old,' said Colin, once he had suppressed his mirth.

'Five *years*!' I gasped. Oh no, I thought, how am I going to hold a five-year-old over the font? I decided to share my concern immediately.

'Five years. Of course. Well, that's splendid,' I said, mustering as much enthusiasm as I could. 'Wonderful. I suppose we've done five-year-olds before, haven't we, Colin?'

'Oh, indeed, yes,' said Colin. I was hoping that he

might have elaborated on the practical considerations covered by this past experience, but instead he buried the lower half of his face in a capacious handkerchief and made several throaty noises.

'Yes,' I said, trying once more to look knowledgeable. 'Five years old! Nothing to it . . . of course . . . a bit big to hold over the font in the normal way. You know, the way we do with babies. So, I will, er, I will, er . . .' I looked towards Colin for some help.

'Use the stepladder,' said Colin smartly.

'That's right,' I said, keen to build on this piece of information. 'I shall stand on a stepladder, so that I can hang young William over the font . . .'

A look of horror had fixed itself on Mrs Kent's face.

'*You* won't be on the stepladder, Father,' said Colin with restrained authority. '*William* will be on the small stepladder so that he can lean over the edge of the font.'

'Yes, yes,' I laughed nervously. 'Just my little joke, you know. I won't actually be *on* the stepladder as such myself, of course. Ha, ha, ha. Had you worried for a moment then, did I, Mrs Kent?'

Mr and Mrs Kent looked at each other as if to say, 'Was this *your* idea or mine?' They then both turned to face Colin, obviously feeling that, of the two of us, he appeared to be slightly more in touch with reality.

'William is at home with his grandmother at the moment. We thought it might be nice if he could come along and see the church before the big day.'

'Splendid idea,' said Colin. 'Don't you think so, Father?'

'Splendid,' I echoed. 'I am a father myself. As it were. You know, not just a "Father", but also a

27

"father". If you know what I mean.' They looked unconvinced, but I ploughed on. 'And so I know what it must mean to a five-year-old. You know, a big old building. Lots of people. A man wearing funny clothes. Having water thrown all over your head. All a bit frightening really!' I ended this small peroration with a laugh.

'You think he'll be *frightened*, then?' said Mrs Kent, the skin tightening visibly around her mouth.

'Not if we get him used to the whole idea of the thing beforehand. If he could come along to the church with you, early one evening, then we could run through the service, and put his little mind at rest about what will happen.'

Colin suggested the following Thursday. Both the Kents were happy with this. I agreed, knowing that I could probably leave work early that afternoon. I was conscious, however, that I would need time to be briefed by the vicar, Canon George, on what I was to do, before I could impart any of this new-found knowledge to poor unsuspecting parishioners. That would have to be fitted in on one, or both, of the following evenings. As Mr and Mrs Kent left the parish office on that first Monday night, I reflected that this was already turning out to be something of a full-time occupation.

By the time I arrived home, Amy was asleep in bed, and neither Cheryl nor I felt much like cooking.

'There's a frozen pizza in the freezer, if you like,' Cheryl called from her desk, where she sat surrounded by piles of essays.

'Why not?' I said, mainly to myself. 'We've got to eat something.'

On the Thursday night I arrived at St Mary's at six o'clock in the evening. I was wearing one of my conventional black clerical shirts under my old and crusty Barbour. I thought it would be a good idea to let young William see me looking like a *real* clergyman.

As I turned into the churchyard I could see Mr and Mrs Kent standing with their son just inside the front porch.

'Hello there,' I called breezily, only to see William take two steps back to hide behind his mother's legs. 'You must be William,' I said, dropping down on one knee and trying to look cuddly. William stared back with a look that said, 'What's it to you, sunshine?', but he spoke not a word.

I led them into the church, which was in complete darkness, and invited them to sit on a pew. At the other end of the church I could see a light coming from the passageway outside the vestry.

'I'll just go and put the church lights on,' I said with confidence. 'Then you'll be able to see what a nice place it is. Not a bit frightening at all, really.'

William poked his head out from under his father's arm, obviously not convinced by the smooth-talking stranger.

When I reached the passageway where the light was on, there was no sign of anyone, so I called out.

'Hello, is there anybody there?'

'I'm here,' came the response. 'It's me. Julie. I'm in the toilet. Do you want to come in?'

I was rather taken aback. Julie was a sixteen-year-old member of the youth group much admired by her male colleagues.

'No. I'm fine, thanks all the same. You go ahead.'

'It's all right,' said Julie. 'I'm painting.'

My mind was suddenly filled with an image of Julie lying on her back on some scaffolding, painting the ceiling of the St Mary's loo, Sistine-chapel-like.

'Jolly good,' I said, backing away. At that point, however, the door of the toilet opened and Julie appeared wearing a pair of bright, white overalls and holding a large paint roller which was dripping magnolia emulsion on the parquet flooring.

'Mum said she'd pay me if I painted the loo. Said she'd got fed up looking at the dirty marks every Sunday morning. Said it'd be her way of giving. By paying me, I mean. You can come in if you like. If you're desperate.'

'Thanks all the same, Julie, but I'm not *desperate*. But you might be able to help me with one thing. I want to put the lights on at the far end of the church. Where the font is. I have to admit that I've never been familiar with all these switches. I don't know which switch relates to which part of the church.'

On the wall was a brass panel on which were about twenty different light switches.

'Do you know, is there one switch that overrides all the others?' I asked.

Julie put down her roller on a sheet of newspaper and came to where I was standing, staring up at the array of switches.

'I think there might be one in here,' she said, reaching towards a small, high cupboard next to the door of the vestry.

In the split-second that it took her to reach up and

open the cupboard, I wanted to say to her:

'Don't touch that cupboard, Julie, because it's alarmed. Which means that you will set off the burglar alarms throughout the church, and I don't yet know how to turn them off.'

Unfortunately, all I managed to say was:

'D . . .'

And then the whole place erupted with the clanging of the St Mary's alarm bells.

I quickly shot one frenzied look in Julie's direction (as if to say, 'Now I'm desperate'), and then ran back out into the church.

Now, lest anyone could have forgotten the predicament that I had got myself into, let me recap. I had invited a young boy of five into the church so that he could get familiar with the place, comfortable with the surroundings, and at ease with the prospect of coming back to be baptized. That young boy was now sitting with his parents in a pitch-black church with alarm bells ringing loudly from every corner.

'I'm most awfully sorry about this,' I called through the gloom. But Mr and Mrs Kent were already beginning to shepherd their snivelling child back towards the main door.

'Please don't go,' I said. 'It won't be like this on the morning of the baptism.'

Mr and Mrs Kent did not look very reassured, but I managed to persuade them that I would 'sort it out' quickly and asked them to bear with me. I called to Julie, who had suddenly appeared at the end of the south aisle, looking like a mysterious vision in her white and slightly luminous overalls.

'Julie,' I shouted above the din of the bells. 'Could you go and get the vicar, please? Fairly quickly if

31

you don't mind. Tell him we've got a little spot of bother with the alarms.' Julie disappeared as quickly as she had appeared.

William was by now making some lamentable groaning noises and I was worried that any attempts at reassurance would only cause him to distrust me even more than he already clearly did. There was nothing for it but to wait for the cavalry, in the rotund shape of Canon George Finney, the vicar of St Mary's and St John's. I shrugged dramatically, and took on that look of complete helplessness that clergymen always seem to do so well.

William was tugging at his mother's coat.

'Mummy, Mummy. I need the toilet. Quickly. Poo. It's coming.'

I was brought back to my senses.

'What? Oh, yes,' I said, in response to Mrs Kent's look of haggard exasperation. 'Along the aisle to where that light is. It's straight in front of you as you go through the first door.'

As they disappeared into the shadows, I turned to apologize once more to Mr Kent, but the words died on my lips as I saw Julie's forlorn shape re-emerging through the doorway. She was accompanied not by the vicar, but by a young police officer.

'Ah!' said the policeman knowingly, on catching sight of my collar. 'I happened to hear the alarms and stopped my car out front, only to find this here young lady hightailing it away from the church and through the gravestones at a rate of knots. She claims to have been doing a spot of painting in the church. Is that right, Vicar?'

Oh, Lord, I thought. Painting!

'Watch out for the wet paint,' I called into the darkness. But it was a forlorn hope. Mother and child had already passed out of the darkness of the church and through the far door to where a light shone ominously in the distance.

* * *

'So what happened next?'

Cheryl sipped her gin and tonic, looking up from her book with her big dark eyes.

'I heard the last trump. The skies opened, and the heavenly hosts cried out in one voice, "Off with his head!".'

'That bad, eh?' said Cheryl, running her fingers through her cropped dark hair and shifting her position on the floor. Her small dancer's body, dressed in denim shirt and jeans, was curled up on a pile of cushions. Her pointed and pixie-like face was screwed up with what I felt to be unconvincing concern. I began to wonder whether she was listening, but I proceeded with the story nevertheless.

'Well, actually, it was worse than that. Mrs Kent got paint on her dress. William poohed himself. Julie was arrested. And Mr Kent hit me.'

'You're not serious!'

Ah, so she *was* listening.

'No, I'm not serious, as it happens,' I said. 'But at that stage it all looked as if the very worst could happen.'

'So come on then,' said Cheryl, a note of slight impatience beginning to creep into her voice. 'What *did* happen?'

I took a mouthful of red wine before continuing.

I told Cheryl how Canon George really *had* saved the day. How he had come into the church by the

33

side door, bumped into Mrs Kent and child, warned them about the paint, turned off the alarm, switched on the lights, and appeared like a veritable angel, walking peacefully towards us with a look of benign benevolence settled across his rosy face.

After the din of that alarm, the sheer silence in the church was blissful. For a few moments the only sound was Canon George's still small voice, speaking in barely more than a whisper, but calming everyone down and putting the whole thing to rights.

Explanations were made to the police officer and to Mr and Mrs Kent. Julie was soon on her way home – already working out, no doubt, a few embellishments for the story that she would tell to the other members of the youth group. Within ten minutes, I was briefing the Kents around the font about the delights that would await us all on the morning of William's baptism.

And William himself? Well, he soon recaptured some of what I can only assume to be his usual charm and started blowing raspberries at me from the top of the infamous stepladder.

I took another mouthful of wine and looked wistfully at the wooden cross that hung from one of the shelves of the oak dresser.

'I don't suppose I'll *always* make such a hash of it,' I said.

'You didn't make a hash of it,' said Cheryl. 'Things just got a bit out of hand, that's all. You're not going to get it all right first time round, anyway.'

'Hm,' I mused, not convinced. And then, after a few moments of silence, I added, 'Why am I doing this?'

'*Why*?' Cheryl said. 'I thought we'd been round

that circle several times already.'

'Yes, I know,' I replied. 'But then it was all so . . . So . . . Oh, I don't know. So *theoretical*, I suppose. And here I am, less than one week "in", so to speak, trying to work out what it's all about. On Sunday I left the cathedral all aglow with the fact of ordination. Twenty-four hours later I'm embroiled in a meeting with a man about frozen pizzas, for goodness' sake. Putting my time and energy into a conversation with a bloke who couldn't care less whether I was a Christian or not. And then there was the whole of yesterday spent trying to calm people down over "Macro-Suds". What am I supposed to be doing?'

'Doing?' Cheryl said, beginning once again to flick through the book. 'Well, for one thing, you shouldn't be taking yourself too seriously.'

'What's *that* supposed to mean?' I said, feeling slightly hurt.

'Not much. Just don't start thinking differently, that's all. Differently to how you did before the do at the cathedral. I don't suppose being a clergyman makes you a better Christian. I'm sure it doesn't make you less inclined to get things wrong. It just puts you on show a bit more.'

'And?' I prompted, after Cheryl had gone back to her book.

'What do you mean "*and*"?'

'Well, aren't you going to say a bit more. Explain your thinking,' I said, feeling that Cheryl was being a bit dismissive of a rather big issue.

'I'm not your analyst, darling,' she replied, looking at me in that sly way that I always found so irresistible. 'Oh, I don't know really. You're on show and so you've got to be ready to respond to people

35

when they come to you for help. As they no doubt will. But you're still the same person in there, under all those silly clothes. You're still going to be struggling to keep the faith – whatever that means – along with everyone else. I don't think you should expect it all suddenly to become crystal-clear just because the bishop's put his hands on your head.'

'Hm,' I said, still unconvinced and feeling a bit got at. But it was late and I didn't feel like a lengthy philosophical discussion about the meaning of life. I rose from my seat, moved across the room, bent down to where she sat, and kissed her warmly on her wide lips.

'You know, darling,' I said, seating myself next to her, 'sometimes I think you see me, and *it*, better than I do. I feel a bit like a man who has been given a costume to wear. Like an animal suit, a giant rabbit, or something. I'm inside, getting all sweaty, trying to do the actions. But I can't actually see whether I'm doing it right.'

'There you go again,' said Cheryl. '*Doing* again. Stop worrying about *doing* it. Just relax a bit. You're only a beginner. If it makes you any happier I'll sew some L-plates on your surplice.'

I laughed and gave her a hug.

'Just remember,' she added, 'you've got all your business and communications experience to fall back on. Perhaps *that's* where your mission lies.'

'Washing powder?' I said, rolling my eyes meaningfully. 'Mulligan and his wretched frozen pizzas? Do me a favour!'

'Well, why not?' she continued. 'Whatever it is that you're trying to point to will be needed by the Mulligans of this world, more than it will by the Kents, I suspect. You'd just better make sure that you're around when they realize they need someone to listen.'

'That's enough,' I said, pulling her closer. 'There's only so much good sense a man can take in one evening. And my brain's beginning to hurt. Let's go to bed.'

'You can go up if you like. I've still got things to do. *And* I need to take up the hem on Amy's new dress. A mother's work is never done.'

'OK, OK, I know when I'm not wanted,' I said, dragging my tired body upright again. 'Goodnight, *mother*.'

Cheryl glowered at me from under her eyebrows with that impish look I knew so well. The look that made me feel that I was not quite in touch with what was going on. That somehow I was an innocent abroad, a child in a grown-up world.

'Goodnight, Father,' she said in a deep husky voice. 'God bless.'

THREE

Keeping Sunday special

*So God blessed the seventh day and
hallowed it, because on it God rested from all
the work that he had done in creation.*
(Genesis 2:3)

CHRISTIAN ministry of one kind or another goes on
all the time, whether or not it happens to be within
a recognizable Christian framework. Sunday mornings, however, are still the occasions when, for most
people, church (and therefore Christian life)
'happens'. On the ten or eleven Sunday mornings
between the ordination and Christmas I began to
understand something more about what actually
did happen, at least at St Mary's and St John's.

The first thing I began to realise as a clergyman,
that I had not fully appreciated as a layman, was
that Sunday morning worship provides lots of
people with roles to play. And heaven help him, or
her, who gets in the way of that role-playing.

On arriving at St Mary's (which claimed much
more of my time than did St John's), I would
invariably bump into the sidesmen — or 'sidespersons' or 'sidespeople', as I was trying to call them.

Doreen Butcher was head 'sidesman' at St Mary's
and in charge of drawing up the rota which allo-
cated three sidespeople for every main service.
These were the folk who would arrange the hymn
books, welcome worshippers on arrival, and take
up the collection halfway through the service.

Doreen was a short, square-set woman in her sixties. Her stiff back, Churchillian expression, and fixed hairdo all helped create a picture of military precision that was only softened slightly by her pink, ornate spectacles and brightly coloured dresses. Doreen, forever resplendent in loud floral patterns, deplored (as you might have imagined) my use of the term 'sidespersons' or 'sidespeople'.

'Michael,' she would say in that helpful tone that only just avoided being patronizing, 'Michael, there are some things, you know, that are beyond sex.'

I said nothing.

'"Sidesman" is one of them,' she continued. 'There is no sex in being a sidesman. It is already an inclusive term. It does not need to be — forgive me — bastardized. It has the same status as "accountant" or "librarian". They too are, in my opinion, without sex. The fact that the word "sidesman" includes the syllable "man" does not change the case.'

Finally I couldn't resist it.

'No sex please, we're sidesmen,' I said.

Doreen was not amused. She made a noise a bit like a rhinoceros clearing its throat, and turned back towards the obsessively neat piles she was making with the hymn books and service sheets.

The head sidesperson was just the first of the St Mary's 'characters' that I would encounter on a normal Sunday morning. Once in the vestry the main focus would be the fearsome presence of the chief sacristan, the person responsible for the clergy vestments and the church silverware. Barbara Bailey was, like Doreen, a woman in her sixties. Sometimes I wondered what the church would do without women in their sixties. Unlike the square and floral figure of Doreen, however, Barbara was tall and always dressed conservatively. Several people had pointed out to me the physiological resemblance that Barbara bore to certain members of the British Royal Family. On these occasions I would simply say 'indeed', or make small simpering noises. I had already decided that Barbara was not someone to meddle with.

As a mere clergyman, I often felt that I was only allowed into the vestry as a result of Barbara's basic good will and sense of fair play. The vestry was without doubt *her* domain and everything that was done there was supposed to be done to the set pattern that Barbara had overseen for some twenty-five years. Everything had its purpose and position, and to question the basis for why things were put in particular places and in particular ways was to question the basis on which God's world had been created. This simple fact alone explained why sacristan and verger were perpetually at loggerheads.

At various intervals Colin the verger would (for reasons best known to himself) tempt fate by rearranging the furniture in the vestry. Not only did this movement in itself represent something of a disruption of the divine order, but (in Barbara's view at least) it left scuff marks on the polished floor. This was, of course, an unforgivable offence and the cause of an ongoing state of cold war, interspersed with the odd unholy row.

On Sunday mornings I would sit in the vestry, feeling nervous about the impending service, and trying to compose my thoughts into something resembling a prayer. Colin would enter, thin and hunched, as if walking into a strong wind. He would be dressed in his black cassock, conscious of needing any available symbol of role and authority. Even this protective dress, however, and his years of similar experiences, could not prevent him from wincing visibly as the chief sacristan swooped on him like a bird of prey.

'Colin!' It was more a bark than a greeting.

'Barbara,' came the reedy and querulous retort, as Colin for the umpteenth time tried to avoid eye contact with his regal antagonist.

On occasions like this, when the air was thick with menace and more than a hint of aggression, I would take myself off to the side chapel where I could be at peace for a few minutes before the service began. In the end, however, I would need to return to the vestry to dress, to be aware of any last-minute arrangements (*most* arrangements were last-minute ones), and to meet those with whom I would be sharing the leadership of the service.

There would be the crucifer (the person who carried the cross), a small weather-beaten man with an eye patch who looked like a pirate. The two young acolytes who would hold the candles, their traditionally cherubic top halves betrayed by the frayed denims and large trainers protruding below their cassocks. Two servers in albs and girdles. Two blue-scarfed readers, side by side in surplices of differing whiteness, and looking like an advertisement for washing powder. The vicar, Canon George, roseate and wide in a capacious chasuble (affectionately known as 'the curtains'). And, of course, myself — the deacon, still looking fresh and uncomfortable in Sunday morning vestments.

Together with the chief sacristan and the verger, you may feel that this group constituted a rather large party to be congregated in the vestry. But there were more still to appear.

A churchwarden, Frank Foster, to return a key borrowed from St John's. A second churchwarden (Alan Watts from St John's) to retrieve the key returned by the first churchwarden. A member of the Mothers' Union to bring a notice of funds raised at a coffee morning. The parish secretary to bring the book with the banns to be read. The Sunday School leader, Penny Wainwright, to ask if the children might bring in their model sheep at the end of the service. Malcolm Potts, the organist, to say, with one minute to go, that surely these aren't the right hymns on the sheet because they're not the ones that the choir was expecting to sing. An unnamed worthy, with less than one minute to go, to ask if anyone had seen the tea strainer.

At the very moment when the atmosphere should have been one of peace and joyous expectation, it would be fraught with hustle, bustle, noise and thinly-veiled impatience. Such was the way we would prepare ourselves for worship on most of those Sundays before Christmas, and many is the time that I reflected on a God who could surely only smile at the vain and inglorious antics of his Lilliputian people.

And yet, for all that, it was worship. Misguided on occasions. Perhaps even shallow at times. But always worship of a sort — not because of what *we* would do, but because of the way in which the Holy Spirit would come into our midst *in spite* of our flawed visions and limited ambitions.

For all the efforts that so many people would put into making it 'work', I often felt that we came nearest to God when the routine mechanics broke down, or at least began to make way for an element of spontaneity. It has to be said that our parish was of a conspicuously ordered tradition. In spite of the tireless efforts of Lynda Soames, there was not too much enthusiasm around for the kind of freer forms of worship adopted by some of the more 'charismatic' churches.

On the whole this in itself was not a problem. Most members of the St Mary's and St John's congregations had been attracted by a style of worship that was defined and predictable. It has to be said, however, that too much order can stifle the working of the Spirit. Certainly, without ever casting myself as a liturgical anarchist, I often felt that in church services, as in life in general, we only ever really become aware of our vulnerability and dependence on God when things don't go according to plan.

Which is just as well really, given some of my early experiences in leading worship as a deacon.

* * *

We were into Advent. Three weeks before Christmas, and I had been given my own distinctive role. I was to be 'in charge' for the first time, and the service was to be a 'special'.

Now, I have to explain straightaway that the word 'special' does not normally conjure up waves of delight within the congregation at St Mary's. Indeed, one stalwart of the church went so far as to indicate to me on another occasion that he'd rather have a hole in the head than have to come to a 'special'. To some extent you might have expected this from what I have already said about the mainly traditional approach adopted for most of the parish services.

It was for this reason that I felt it something of a dubious honour to have been given the responsibility of organizing and running this particular 'special'. When it had first been mooted, about the time of my ordination, I had tried to indicate to Canon George that this was perhaps not necessarily the best way to establish my liturgical credentials with the regular churchgoers.

Canon George had smiled that youthful smile of his and said, on the contrary, he could think of no better way to 'launch' me (yes, I'm sure he used the word 'launch') on an unsuspecting public.

I opined that, far from being unsuspecting, I felt that members of the St Mary's congregation were in fact *very* suspecting, and that they were likely to carry on suspecting me of all sorts of crimes if they saw that I had been put in charge of 'specials'.

'You have not been put in charge of "specials",' said Canon George. 'Just this *particular* "special". Of course, were to to go down swimmingly well, then I'm sure that everyone would want more from you. But we must do things gently. Not too much at a time. After all, I do have to think of Cheryl and Amy. I don't want them to feel that we're making too many demands on your valuable time.'

I nodded. Canon George's phrase 'go down swimmingly' had, for some reason, brought to mind a picture of the *Titanic*. I wondered if the opposite phrase might be to 'go down drowningly'.

And so it was that I had spent several hours here and there during October and November trying to pull together some ideas for the 'special'. My plan was not to change too much; the service would follow the usual format of a Sunday morning at St Mary's. Within that framework, however, I felt that there was scope for involving children and families a bit more. I set out to include the 'uniformed movements', as they were unattractively labelled —

that is the Cubs, Brownies, Beavers, and so on, who were affiliated to the church. I also wanted to include children from our own St Mary's Sunday School. The theme was to be 'Light and Darkness'. It must have seemed like a good idea at the time.

The centrepiece of the service was to be a slide presentation. I had spent much of the previous four weeks getting together the material for this by using various resources, including the 35mm slide library at the advertising agency. For this particular service the congregation were to be initiated into the delights of back projection, and I had spent most of Saturday afternoon establishing the optimal positions for the projector and screen within the confines of the sanctuary.

The screen measured about six feet by four feet and was portable. My plan was to balance this on top of the communion rail at the front of the sanctuary. The projector would be on a stand about four or five feet beyond the screen. Having finally found the perfect setup, I marked the position of the projector stand by sticking four pieces of Elastoplast onto the buff-coloured carpet. These, I hoped, would ensure that the projector could be moved into position quickly, and without much fuss, at the appropriate point in the service.

The morning of the service dawned, and a foul morning it was as well. Rain was falling in a steady and heavy way from a dark grey sky, and it looked as if there could be worse to come. The choir and sanctuary party assembled in the side chapel ready for the procession out into the body of the church. The organ had begun the introduction to 'O come, O come, Emmanuel' when I heard Iris Dobbs, the widest chorister this side of the Urals, telling her neighbour in a 'what's the world coming to' manner that Barbara Bailey had just found several pieces of Elastoplast stuck all over the sanctuary carpet.

'Fortunately,' added Iris, 'there was time to remove them before anyone could notice.'

I counted to ten. Slowly. And then tried to turn my scream into the first verse of the hymn.

The party moved out. At the head was our piratical crucifer, followed by about twenty members of the choir, robed and in twos. Then came the rest of us: readers, servers, acolytes, clergy. As we made our way in a stately fashion along the north aisle of the church my mind was racing. What was I going to do? Would I be able to remember, or guess, where the projector and screen were to be positioned? Behind me I could hear the deep resonant sound of Canon George's bass voice. Would he sing so blithely, I asked myself, if he knew the torment I was in already?

We turned at the font into the nave and, being the penultimate person in the procession, I was almost the last to see the next catastrophe that lay ahead of us. The uniformed movements had wanted to parade their flags at the beginning and the end of the service, and 'colour parties' had been appointed to do the honours. These colour parties were to be positioned at the end of the nave (that is, at the back of the church) so that they could join the procession at a discreet distance behind the rest of us.

I can only assume that my very clear instructions had been misunderstood. The colour parties had assembled at our entry, and had done so at the end of the nave — but, regrettably, at the wrong end. Which meant that crucifer and choir now found their way to the sanctuary blocked by a motley crew

of flag-waving Cubs and Brownies. The immediate result was that the whole procession ran into itself, concertina-like. This inelegant arrest was then followed by much wild gesticulation by members of the choir on the one hand, and the respective leaders of the uniformed movements on the other.

The outcome of this slightly frenzied gesturing was that the green and brown sea parted, and the choir was able to thread its way in a rather untidy fashion through the flags, the embarrassed adult looks, and the children's grins. At one point I remember noticing that there was a loud shriek (alto, I think) from somewhere about fifteen bodies ahead of me, and the main talk in the choir vestry after the whole lamentable affair was of how Iris had 'very nearly had her eye put out by one of those wretched flag-poles'.

Finally, stationed next to Canon George on the chancel step, and facing the congregation, I was to find that there would be no let-up in the 'specialness' of this service.

Canon George opened wide his arms, smiled, and said in as breezy a way as he could manage:

'The . . . be . . . you.'

What he actually said, of course, was 'The Lord be with you', but the microphones had obviously decided that this would be a special day for them as well.

St Mary's is a big church and, when the heating fans are churning away, it is difficult to hear anything unless a microphone is being used. Canon George and I both wore radio microphones clipped to our vestments, with the transmitters strapped to our belts underneath. Admittedly, we had had a few problems with them in the past, but not normally so obviously — and certainly not so obviously near the beginning of the service.

My face must have already been a picture of panic as I looked sideways at Bill, one of the readers and the sort of man who looks as if he would be at home with a screwdriver.

'It's probably the transmitter,' said Bill in a very loud stage whisper. 'Try fiddling with his thing.'

I turned back towards Canon George, but he (like an old pro) did not want to give the impression of being dependent on technology. He was pushing gamely ahead with his words of introduction, presumably on the basis that someone or something would correct the fault before very long. His ability to be completely unflustered by such goings-on was quite uncanny, but I could already see the pained looks spreading across the faces of the congregation, as they struggled to work out what he was saying.

'It's . . . to . . . you . . . on . . . beautiful . . . morning.'

And so on.

There was nothing for it. I would have to act on Bill's advice. I turned slightly towards Canon George, slipped my hand under the chasuble, and tried to find the transmitter fixed to the belt of his trousers. As the Canon stopped momentarily to look askance at me, I realized that he had the transmitter in his trouser pocket. I took a deep breath and pushed my hand down into his trouser pocket in the hope that my fingers would soon alight on the switch, and that I would be able to check that it was in the correct 'on' position.

It was there all right, and it seemed that the switch was not fully engaged. But at the moment of correction I must have accidentally tickled Canon George's leg, because he suddenly doubled up (with my hand still in his pocket) and pitched forward onto the carpet, taking me with him.

There was at first a stunned silence from everyone. Then a few titters, which finally broke out into widespread and nervous laughter once it had been established that the two of us had not been hurt, and were not subject to some kind of joint, concerted and uncontrollable fit.

As I wrestled myself free of the Canon and his voluminous robes, I found myself being helped to my feet by a bevy of concerned and amused parishioners.

For his part, Canon George took the whole thing very well. Once in a vertical position again, he beamed at his audience, and explained through his now perfectly working microphone that he had never before had a clergyman down his trousers. I could tell from his immediate look of remorse that he hadn't meant it in quite the way it was understood by many of those present. But he capped that rather questionable comment with the witty aside that it wasn't necessarily all bad having the parish deacon in your pocket.

We managed to get through the first part of the service without any further problems, and then it came to the slide presentation. By now I had had time to work out my plan of action, and so I stepped forward, switched on my microphone and began to talk to the assembled company.

'Right. Well, we shall now be having a slide presentation on the subject of "Light and Darkness". First of all I will have to locate the required position for the projector. So, if you will excuse me, I shall try to find the appropriate markings on the carpet. Thank you.'

I was banking on the fact that there might be some residual marks or identations on the carpet where the pieces of Elastoplast had been. Switching off my microphone again I fell to my knees in the sanctuary and began scrabbling around in search of some evidence that a projector stand had once occupied a position there. Perhaps it was because of my desperation to find *something* that, after only a few seconds, I fancied I had identified two clear markings on the carpet, and so I instructed the servers to set up the stand as we had originally planned.

The screen was balanced on the communion rail, and we were ready to start. Unfortunately it became clear with the very first slide that something was out of position. I had a choice; either to try to reposition the projector and its stand, or to move the screen.

Even as I made my choice, I knew instinctively that it was the wrong one.

I waved at a couple of bored Cubs in the front row, and coaxed them out of the pew to lend a hand. I asked each of them to hold one side of the screen and to move very slowly towards the congregation until the first picture came into focus. By this time the members of the congregation had fully entered into the spirit of the 'special' occasion, and were calling bits of advice from the body of the church.

'Back a bit.'

'To your left.'

'Up a bit.'

And so on.

Needless to say, this all added to the general amusement, and the atmosphere was once more punctuated with various titters and bursts of half-concealed laughter.

Once the screen had been talked into position, I handed over to the Sunday School. The idea was that several children from the Sunday School would read from a text I had prepared, while one of the leaders took charge of moving the projection carousel on from one slide to the next. This was a process which, as you might imagine, required a modicum of co-ordination.

Now, so that you may begin to anticipate what happened, I need to explain the basic idea behind the presentation that I had put together. During October I had spent some time with the Sunday School listening to what they had been covering during the previous few weeks. I then tried to take those themes and stories and include them in a framework which basically juxtaposed ideas of

'Light' and 'Darkness'. Some of the visuals were literally pictures of light and darkness, but many were more figurative contrasts — in the world of play, sport, everyday life, and even politics and the world situation. It was a fairly simple plan really. On the one hand *this*, but on the other hand *that*. And so on. Simple, that is, provided you did not get the sequencing out of kilter.

Within a few slides of the introduction, Jeremy, a rather over-confident child in my opinion, had managed to omit one critical piece of text. Meanwhile, Charlene (one of the assistant Sunday School teachers) continued to plough ahead by changing the visuals at each pregnant pause.

The consequences were either dismal, or hilarious, depending on your point of view and state of mind. For some three minutes, each image of 'Light' was accompanied by a statement about 'Darkness', and vice versa.

OK, you may say, but surely the Reverend Michael Dunn, so-called expert in communications, could have stepped in to save the day. Well, yes, I *could* have done that. But the trouble was that the situation always looked as if it was about to put itself right. You must know that feeling. When you don't act because it looks as if things are going to get themselves back on track without any intervention.

So, I'm naive. I admit it. But for a while it really *did* look as though Charlene and Jeremy were going to move back together. And so I did nothing, but squirmed and prayed. And, of course, the more the congregation felt free to laugh at the pointedly inappropriate contrasts made by the presentation, the less I felt like intervening.

Finally by some fluke of timing (don't ask me

how), the words and the pictures came back into a state of synchronization, and the last five-minute section of the presentation went as planned. But by then whatever serious intent we had once aspired to had disappeared in a quagmire of incompetence.

Having said that, the end of the presentation was met with a burst of spontaneous applause — something which had never greeted the end of any other presentation or sermon in St Mary's. Even if this applause had been occasioned by a feeling of sympathy, it nevertheless managed to cheer me considerably, and so I threw myself into the Sharing of the Peace with abandon and an unusual degree of warmth.

From then on I had too much to do to spend time replaying the real and imagined horrors of the first half of the service. I took my position behind the altar and began to prepare for the Eucharist by laying out the corporal (a square white cloth) and preparing to receive the bread and wine which would be put on it.

Outside the rain seemed to have become even heavier, and I could hear a monotonous drumming on the guttering just outside the east window. Canon George was well into the Eucharistic Prayer when the first drop of water fell from the high ceiling and landed with an almost imperceptible sound in the middle of the sanctuary, about six feet in front of the altar.

This really was a morning of firsts, for (again) I could not recall an occasion when a roof leak had played quite such a prominent role in the shape of the liturgy. Spying the problem, one of the servers disappeared through a side door for a few moments, before re-emerging with a tin waste-paper bin which was then placed in the middle of the carpet, directly under the place from which the leak seemed to have sprung.

This was all very well, and no doubt was a good way both to mark the leak, and also to prevent it doing any unnecessary and insidious damage to the sanctuary. However, it also meant that every six seconds a fairly loud 'ker-doink' echoed from the front of the church as the drips hit the bottom of the bin.

Had this been the only sign from the heavens, then I think we could have probably all convinced ourselves that we had got off fairly lightly. With the bin in place, we continued with the prayers up to the point where Canon George and I stood in front of the altar ready to administer the bread and wine to those around us. Canon George stood holding the ciborium, the silver vessel in which were the consecrated wafers, and I stood holding the chalice full of wine.

Perhaps there really *was* no clap of thunder at this point. Perhaps it is just that my imagination has added that as a small embellishment to my recollection of events. But, thunder or no thunder, it was then that the moment of divine intervention really did seem to occur, as a large droplet of rain (presumably from another leak) fell plumb into the middle of the chalice that I was holding.

I was stunned and took one step back with a mixture of horror and delight fighting for control of my emotions. In a split second my mind filled with the private prayer that I had said quietly to myself only minutes before when preparing the chalice.

O God, who didst wonderfully create, and yet more wonderfully renew the dignity of man's

nature: grant that by the mystery of this water and
wine we may be made partakers of his divinity,
who vouchsafed to share our humanity, Jesus
Christ thy Son our Lord.

Dignity. Dignity. The word reverberated in my head.
No doubt I would be roundly condemned for my
running of this 'special'. It would be seen as the
antithesis of dignified worship. Even the thunder-
storm would be laid at my door. Something I should
have anticipated. Not to mention the holes in the
roof.

And yet, I could not help asking myself, wasn't
there perhaps something dignified about accepting
that the human lot was, indeed, one of plans gone
awry, of cockups, of trying to make the best of it, of
laughter in the face of apparent catastrophe? Wasn't
that what Jesus had shared in, by being part of
humanity? And wasn't that perhaps something of a
clue in helping us to go beyond ourselves in search
of the divine?

Canon George's polite coughs became more
urgent, and I was called back to reality with a start.
In front of us the people were beginning to line up
to be fed, and we had work to do.

* * *

'I think you did very well,' said Canon George.
'Considering.'

I looked back at him sheepishly.

'Considering what?' I asked.

He thought for a moment before saying:

'God rested on the seventh day, of course.
Sometimes I think he still does. If *I* were God, that
would be the day *I'd* take off.'

FOUR

A star is born

When they saw that the star had stopped,
they were overwhelmed with joy.
(Matthew 2:10)

CHRISTMAS comes but once a year — thank God!

As far as the local shopping centre is concerned, it seems to come during the first week of October and to stay for about three months, blurring indistinguishably into the January sales. I've always been somewhat unmoved by autumn windows full of tinsel and fairy lights, and have studiously tried to ignore the tortuous, and largely commercial, Christmas preparations. This had clearly not been so easy to do over the last couple of years, with Amy remorselessly counting off the days and then the hours until that moment when Father Christmas would arrive to half-eat the one mince pie, and drink the small glass of sherry, that we would so thoughtfully leave for him in the hallway.

For my first year in holy orders, Christmas really started with the singing of carols by candlelight at the service of nine lessons and carols which took place about a week before Christmas Day. Modelled on the service which was yearly broadcast from King's College, Cambridge, the St Mary's version attracted a large number of local people, and it was with great excitement that I saw the church so full of expectant faces.

At the beginning the church was in darkness and,

as people arrived, everyone was given a white candle as well as a service sheet. The candles (all of which were, at that point, unlit) each had a round collar of white card which was supposed to catch the melting wax.

Once everyone was assembled, facing forward in the body of the dark church, the choir entered through the back door carrying candles that were alight. The single voice of a young chorister began to sing 'Once in Royal David's City', and the whole choir then slowly made its way forward in procession, along the nave, whilst the two churchwardens followed behind, lighting the candles of the congregation row by row. As the members of the choir reached the chancel step, they moved forward to take their places on a large semi circle of chairs which had been placed at the front of the church, a few feet from where I was sitting in the vicar's stall.

Seen from there, the overall effect was very impressive; the singing came closer and closer and the church began to be filled with light, as the flames from the candles were passed forward from one pew to the next. By the third verse, everyone in the church was singing together whilst holding a lighted candle.

It was a display of simple and compelling unity, as the joy and expectation, mystery and wonder were all felt edging forward through the building, spreading from one person to another, irresistible and insistent. Here, you might have said, was the coming of the Light of the World. Then again, for many, this may have been Yuletide come unto St Mary's, with the flicker of an old-world flame, the warmth of an open fireside, and the glow of a traditional greetings card.

Whatever else Christmas may be to those who choose to keep it, it is often a time when human vulnerability and human mishaps come to the fore and are granted centre stage. If the various spirits of Christmas can sometimes take us beyond ourselves, then the practicalities of Christmas often seem to bring about uncomfortable realities. It is perhaps fitting that the part of the Christian year which focuses on the incarnation of God in human form, is also a time when we can see so clearly some of the most fragile aspects of humanity.

David Parfitt was everyone's idea of a perfect young chorister. Blond-haired, rosy-cheeked, and with the voice (some would say) of an angel. Dressed in his cassock, surplice and bright white ruff he looked every inch the Christmas-card choirboy as he took his position at the lectern for the first of the nine readings.

As David was a boy of small stature, Colin the verger had provided a wooden box on which he could stand so that he was able to reach the microphone. So there he stood, his candle alight in one hand, straining slightly forward to see over the top of the lectern at the admiring and warmly-lit faces below.

I observed that he read very well, although my own attention was rather more engaged by the fact that he had pushed the cardboard collar of the candle up towards the flame, so that it seemed in danger of catching light.

At the end of the reading David said, 'Thanks be to God', switched off the microphone, and turned away from the lectern. What happened next happened very quickly.

As he moved towards the edge of the box to step

down, the box tipped up and David was launched towards the rest of the choir at an angle and a speed that no one was expecting. This precipitous change of position was finally enough for the cardboard collar to be ignited by the flame of the candle, and David suddenly found himself with a flaring torch in his hand.

His natural reaction was to try to cast away the torch as soon as he felt the heat of the flames, but at that moment his foot struck against the chancel step and he was propelled headlong towards the floor. In a second the flames had licked up at the edge of his surplice, and there was a great gasp from everyone present when it seemed as if a tragic combustion were about to take place before our very eyes.

The gasp was followed by a scraping of chairs, and the sound of heavy thuds. No sooner had David's surplice begun to smoulder and catch fire than it was extinguished by two large members of the choir who threw themselves on the nascent flames, swamping the boy with their capacious bodies.

The whole incident was over within a few seconds, and it was only after the event that any of us allowed ourselves to think what might have happened if the garments of the two gallant saviours had also caught fire. Thank God, that did not happen.

Iris Dobbs aside, Cynthia Jarrett and Jim Barstow were probably the widest and heaviest members of the choir. Certainly they were not people renowned for their fleetness of foot prior to this act. But, fortunately on this occasion, their bodies moved as fast as their brains, and between them they proved to be the quickest thirty stones on four legs.

David was extricated from beneath their formidable masses suffering from no more than a few hefty bruises, and a slightly sprained wrist where he had fallen awkwardly. The front of his surplice, however, bore testimony to what might have been a far worse fate.

At the moment when Cynthia and Jim landed on top of David, everyone in the church had stood up, and many of the congregation now crowded around the front of the church as concern changed to naked relief and then to heartfelt thanksgiving. David's mother had been one of the first to spring forward at the critical moment, and she was now leading her son out to the vestry where he could be checked over by the several people with medical and first-aid knowledge who had immediately made themselves known.

Canon George, who had had nothing to do until that point in the service, now came forward, exuding his usual blend of calm and good sense, to suggest that everyone should extinguish his or her candle. Most people had by then already done so, and soon the church lights were on once more, and people were making their way back to their places.

David soon reappeared with his mother to assure everyone that all was well. Cynthia and Jim, looking flushed from both their exertions and also from the justifiable plaudits they had earned, took up their places again with the choir. Gradually a feeling of great peace and blessed relief spread itself over the whole place, and the service picked up where it had left off.

Throughout the whole episode I had been no more than an observer, marooned in the vicar's stall at the side of the sanctuary. But, as an observer, my heart too had raced with the expected pain, and now sighed with the deliverance that had been granted.

The candles may have been blown out, but a brighter light was shining, and (for those of us, at least, gathered at St Mary's on that December evening) the darkness had not been able to overcome it.

* * *

The following day was a Monday and I had arranged to take a day's holiday from the advertising agency. My main objective was, finally, to do some Christmas shopping, but I had also arranged to make a pastoral visit at nine o'clock. As the woman I was visiting (Mrs Brocklebank) was a fairly 'traditional' lady of the congregation, I felt it would be proper if I wore a dog collar, and so I put on one of my less exuberant clerical shirts.

With no early morning train to catch, I was able to take Amy to school — although this proved to be less of an unalloyed pleasure than I had imagined. If I needed any reminding that this was the first time I had taken Amy to school whilst wearing a dog collar, then I received it almost as soon as we left the house. Amy stuck out her bottom lip, and looked up at me accusingly from below her small furrowed brow.

'I don't mind really, Daddy,' she said, in that condescending tone that seems to come so naturally to five-year-olds. '*I* know you're not a *real* vicar. *I* know you're a *silly* vicar.'

I nodded appreciatively at the implied compliment.

'But Jessica and Beatrice,' she continued confidentially, 'might think you're a *proper* vicar.'

Oh, the shame of it, I thought.

'And is that bad?' I asked, somewhat naively.

Any rolled her eyes in that 'Will parents never learn?' way.

'Yeeeees,' she said with prolonged emphasis. 'Of course. I told them you make adverts on the television.'

'And that's all right, is it?' I said.

'Course it is,' she replied, as if choosing to overlook my obvious stupidity.

'But being a vicar *isn't* all right?'

'Course not,' she said crossly. 'It's the pits.'

I thought, I don't believe this. My daughter of just five years has told me that my spiritual and pastoral vocation is 'the pits'. Where on earth does she get these expressions from? Certainly not from *me*, I decided. The pits indeed!

A few seconds later we had turned the corner and were beginning to walk along the road which led to South House School, where Amy had been a pupil for just over three months. At that moment my daughter suddenly sprinted away and then resumed her leisurely walk about twenty feet ahead of me.

'It's all right,' she called back. 'They might not see you if you walk behind.'

Thanks a lot, I thought. I'd anticipated that I might be an embarrassment to my daughter *one* day, but had assumed that it would be when she was about sixteen. I had not expected parental marginalization to arrive quite as early as this.

'Look', I called back, vaguely aware that my next comments were likely to signal a defeat which would set a pattern for the next fifteen years. 'I'll do you a deal. I'll button my coat right up to the top and keep my chin down, if you'll come back here, walk along with me, and generally be prepared to acknowledge me as your parent.'

Even though some of my words brought a puzzled look to her face, she quickly picked up my drift when I converted intent into action.

'OK,' she said, 'it's a deal.'

And with that grand gesture of magnanimity, she waited for me to catch up with her.

I told the story to Mrs Brocklebank as she made me a cup of herbal tea. I had only ever drunk herbal tea once before, and had vowed then never to drink it again. Mrs Brocklebank had suggested it, however, with the zeal of a convert, and I had not felt inclined to fly in the face of such evident enthusiasm so early in the morning.

'My father was a clergyman,' she said to me over the top of her glasses.

I should have guessed, I thought.

'Never did *me* any harm,' she continued, in a way that suggested that Amy should be taken in hand for such a blatant display of disloyalty. After a few momemts of silence, however, in which we both chewed on our raspberry-coloured tea, she added:

'Mind you, clergy were respected in *those* days.'

I nodded back whilst I tried to think of ways in which I might be able to swallow the wretched concoction without having to taste it.

'No more, I'm afraid,' she said, and I started to

brighten up, thinking that she was referring to the tea. But no. She was still harping on about how clergy were not respected. I sucked the toxic liquid through my teeth whilst trying to work out whether her comments were critical of clergy or of everybody else.

'More tea?' The question I had been dreading.

'Well, I really must be getting along, if you don't mind. It was really very . . . Well, very . . . Different, really, I suppose. But I don't think I'll have another. Thanks all the same.'

I had been with her for about three-quarters of an hour, and we had cleared up the personal matter on which she had asked me to call within the first fifteen minutes. I left her happily enough planning the brew for the visit that afternoon of the flower-arranging committee, and I strode off towards the shops in the hope of finding a present for Cheryl.

As I only wear a dog collar on rare occasions other than church services, I always find it interesting to note people's reactions to it. That morning spent at the local shopping centre, whilst being unusual in some ways, provided the sort of spectrum of reactions that I was to grow accustomed to. Most of these reactions were clear in people's faces without ever a word passing their lips.

Reaction number one. 'Oh no, it's a vicar. Quick, look the other way or he'll start telling you how Jesus loves you, and trying to convert you.' This reaction was to be found amongst all social types and ages, both male and female, and implied a distrust which could well be deep-seated and dangerous.

Reaction number two. 'That's nice. Look dear, it's a young clergyman. Isn't that nice?' This reaction was to be found predominantly among older women and implied a trust which was likely to be as deep-seated and dangerous as the *distrust* of the previous group.

Reaction number three. 'Yawn, yawn. What a boring old so-and-so a clergyman is.' This reaction was to be found predominantly among younger people, and was based, I feel sure, on a certain amount of supporting evidence.

Reaction number four. 'Here comes a member of that authoritarian, repressive, out-of-touch, conservative, story-telling, truth-warping, narrow-minded, intellectually bankrupt, morally corrupt, hypocritical, mealy-mouthed bourgeois institution known as the Church.' This reaction was also to be found predominantly among younger people, and was based on several hundred years of supporting evidence.

All these reactions, plus several others, I encountered during my first half hour in and out of the various shops before I entered the retailing temple of St Michael.

For most of the people most of the time in our parish, the service they get from St Michael is always likely to be more important than the service they get from St Mary or St John. Any conversation with almost any member of the parish would have left you with the impression that Marks & Spencer had advanced in people's perceptions from being the only place for socks and pants, to being the inventor of the sandwich. Indeed, some of the more passionate adherents of the chain store might have you believe that, in the days before Marks & Spencer food, it was both impossible to buy proper bread or fresh fruit anywhere, and hell on earth to organize a dinner party.

Don't get me wrong — I'm not knocking it. As a professional communicator and self-proclaimed marketing specialist, I suppose I'm jealous of any organization's ability to make itself appear indispensable. Once the church wakes up to the fact that it *too* is in competition for the hearts and minds of people, then we might begin to see something that can grip people's imagination.

As it happens, on this particular day my mission at M&S was one of the more traditional ones. Underwear. I made my way up the escalator and headed towards the ladies' lingerie department in search of some skimpy items for Cheryl.

Society may have progressed to the stage where the idea of a man buying ladies' underwear is not *simply* a matter of concealed laughter and worried looks, but evidently the prospect of a *clergyman* undertaking such a task is still one to be greeted with elbow nudging and sidelong glances. OK, OK, I don't want to appear to be taking myself *too* seriously — and the two young ladies obviously enjoyed baiting me — but even so . . .

I admit it. My posture *may* have looked a little ludicrous, kneeling, as I was, on the floor with a brassiere in each hand. And I had already become aware of the two young women exchanging comments a few feet to my left before one of them actually spoke to me.

'Excuse me.'

I looked up to find a young, round-faced woman smiling angelically down at me. She had a wide mouth with deep red lipstick and short spiky black hair, and she was wearing a leather jacket. A yard or two behind her was her blonde friend, trying to keep a straight face.

'Excuse me,' she said again. 'Are you all right down there?'

'Yes,' I said. 'I think so. Why do you ask?'

'Well, you looked a bit stuck, that's all.'

The blonde friend was now giggling, and looking away.

'No, I'm not stuck. Thanks all the same,' I said getting to my feet rather inelegantly, still clutching a brassiere in either hand.

'*I've* got one of those,' she said, pointing at the skimpier of the two items.

'Really,' I replied, trying hard not to look at her chest.

'Yeah. It's really nice. She'll like that. Looks better in black, though.'

'Right,' I said, smiling and taking one step back. 'Well, thanks very much. That was . . . er . . . that was . . . er . . . good of you to mention it.'

'That's all right. No trouble. It's just that you looked a bit stuck, that's all.'

'Right,' I said again, bending down to replace the rejected garment on the stand, and waving the recommended item jauntily in her direction. 'Merry Christmas!'

So what was I supposed to say? The young woman smiled at me cheekily before echoing my 'Merry Christmas' and moving away with her giggling friend. Holding the chosen design in my hand, I turned away to find the equivalent item in black. I then picked out (single-handedly) a pair of matching panties, and took the booty over to the desk in order to pay.

I'm always impressed when the sales staff at M&S tell you what you're buying. Some might find it off-putting, but I have to say that on at least one occasion I have been prevented from buying the wrong size socks by the assistant reading the size label immediately prior to ringing up the amount. On this particular morning, however, I felt more than usually conscious of this attention.

The middle-aged woman at the till had a broad Irish accent and probably thought she was being polite and respectful as she loudly intoned:

'That's a 34B then, Father.'

'Yes,' I said approvingly, as if some confirmation were necessary.

It may have been a coincidence, but at that moment the woman behind me snorted. What the hell, I thought. I'm liberated. I'm a new man. Don't judge me by appearances. I am a smooth man. An advertising man. They don't come smoother.

But even as I walked away, gripping tightly my green plastic bag, I knew that things were not that simple, and were never likely to be. On occasions like this, what people saw in me was the collar rather than the person — and the collar often stood for a whole load of baggage that I could only struggle to understand.

As in so many areas, what lies under the surface is fraught with taboo.

* * *

Christmas Day came at last. Having young children can sometimes have its advantages. Largely, I think, on Amy's account, I was excused Midnight Mass and the early morning service at eight o'clock. I was, however, on duty for the nine-thirty service — preaching as well as fulfilling my role as deacon. As I had gone to bed late on Christmas Eve I was slightly concerned that it would prove difficult to get up, have Amy open her presents, and get the three of us to St Mary's for about nine fifteen.

I shouldn't have worried. Amy woke us at six-thirty and so we found ourselves with plenty of time to do eveything that she would have wanted and expected before we all took ourselves off to church.

As we climbed into the car I began to wonder how old she would be before she realized that most normal children did not go to church as regularly as *she* did. Presumably, I thought, if she's already sensitive about school friends seeing her with a dog-collar-wearing father, it won't be long.

We had already taken her to St Mary's during the afternoon of Christmas Eve for the crib service. This was the service especially designed for children, involving the singing of carols and the placing of some rather large and gaudy papier-mâché figures in a crib scene. The crib scene was positioned, rather awkwardly I felt, in the middle of the sanctuary, directly in front of the altar. Some well-intentioned soul had at some time obviously wanted to make it the focal point of the church over the Christmas period and, whilst I had no particular objection to the sentiment behind it, its cumbersome presence (alongside that of a large and forlorn-looking Christmas tree) made the sanctuary look rather too much like a cluttered shop window.

Sticking up from the roof of the model stable was a three-foot rod of iron. From the top of the rod sprouted a piece of wire about six inches long, and on top of this was a star. Any slight movement to the crib started a vibration that would work its way up the iron rod, finally making the star on the end of the wire sway from side to side. When you consider that the star was unfortunately positioned to be in line with the head of anyone standing behind the altar, then you may begin to imagine the potential of the situation.

As we arrived for the crib service on that Christmas Eve, various children had been given figures which they would be invited to take up to the sanctuary and the crib scene at the appropriate moment in the Christmas story, as it was retold by a succession of readers. Veterans of former crib services at St Mary's knew that the secret was to arrive at the church early in order to 'bag' the best figures. As we arrived late, there was nothing left for Amy to take up, although the daughter of one of the choir members offered her a half share in a shepherd.

This allocation of papier-mâché figures was the cause of a certain amount of argument and some mischief. A couple of those who had received a chicken or a sheep began to grow aggressive towards those who had been given Mary, Joseph or a wise man. Indeed, the three wise men were considered to be the prime catch in the whole proceedings, as they were clearly taller and noticeably more colourful than any of the other figures.

It was this fact, no doubt, that vexed young Craig, who had been designated as the carrier of the ass. Sliding malevolently and insidiously away from his minder and along his pew, he made several attempts to wrestle Balthasar from the hands of Geoffrey, a stout little boy with cropped hair and no front teeth. Geoffrey's patience finally snapped and, with great gusto, he whacked Craig around the head with Balthasar, dislodging the wise man's head so that it fell to the floor and rolled unceremoniously along the nave.

The immediate result of this fracas was that Geoffrey was frog-marched away from the pews by a mortified mother, and Craig was left to leer in a most unseemly manner at the guardians of Melchior and Caspar. Amy pointed out to me in her own way after the service that this hardly seemed like justice, and I tried to make some comment about how unfair life can be. In fact, I think my actual words were something to do with asses triumphing over wise men. I remember that because, as I said it, Cheryl gave me one of those withering looks as if to say 'Oh, for heaven's sake'.

The reason for mentioning all this in the context of Christmas morning was the inescapable centrality of that crib scene. That crib scene was destined to become, for me at least, a very tangible reminder of the state of the church. On that Christmas morning, of course, the three wise men were not themselves positioned at the side of the baby Jesus. They were over at the very edge of the sanctuary — on their journey, as it were. And such a long journey, figuratively speaking. Over the period between Christmas Day and Epiphany, those figures would be moved gradually closer to the babe each day until the time when finally they would arrive. Not a moment too soon.

This may well have met with approval from the literalists among the congregation, but it was the cause of great puzzlement to those children who had been brought up to believe that all were there — shepherds and kings, simple and wise — at the same time. It was also something of a distraction from the crib scene itself, because the three wise men stuck out rather more prominently than perhaps they should have done by being positioned so completely on their own.

The dramatic impact of this divided scene was heightened on this particular Christmas Day by the fact that one of the wise men seemed to be holding his head at a rather jaunty angle. Colin had done his best with the sticky tape and the Superglue, I dare say, but poor old Balthasar was never to be the same again.

These images conjured up a host of disruptive thoughts in my head. With this service still to get through, I tried to expunge the memories of the crib service from my mind. I tried to ignore what now seemed to be a set of intrusive and questioning figures, and to concentrate on the liturgy that lay ahead.

The church was very nearly full, and I was happy to see so many unfamiliar faces amongst the congregation. Despite any concerns I might have been harbouring, everything seemed to go smoothly enough – although I couldn't help smiling at Canon George's jerky movements behind the altar during the Eucharistic Prayer, as he tried to make the bread and wine visible from behind the tinsel of a Star of Bethlehem that, unprovoked, swayed from side to side in front of him.

I found I could look at nothing else, and I remember thinking 'as long as everyone remembers that the *real* star is Jesus, then we're OK'. It was nevertheless a joy, and also a relief, when the swaying died down and the star finally stopped.

When the service was ended, I stood outside the main door with Canon George, as the weak sun struggled to add a glow to the bleak and milky sky. Saying 'good morning' and 'Happy Christmas' to all the new faces as they left the church was, I found, an experience of conflicting and mixed emotions. Of course, it was a joy to see them all there. But *why*, I kept asking myself? Why *were* they there? What *exactly* was it about Christmas Day that had brought them along? And how did it relate to faith in a wider context?

I mentioned my thoughts, naturally enough, to Canon George — but he only said, 'Well, everyone loves Christmas and the birth of a baby', and that wasn't the sort of response I had been looking for. I was suddenly swept away with the absolute knowledge of how little we understood about the motivations of our parishioners. In a world where I knew, only too well, that companies were spending millions of pounds to understand every last detail about how their consumers *thought*, and why they *acted* in the way they did, the church knew so little about its *own* consumers.

I blinked up at a heaven drained of colour and reflected that my quarrel (if quarrel it was) was with the church and not with God. I would not — could not — allow a note of despair to disturb a day of great happiness and great potential. But equally, I resolved, I would return to the subject later, even if it took me years to work out what exactly it was that needed to be said and done. For the moment, however, I determined simply to be thoughtful and, I hope, prayerful.

Even so, one key question kept banging away inside my head: how can an institution that puts so much store by symbols and stories be so relatively uninterested in what those symbols and stories really mean to people?

With the voices singing in my ears that this was all folly, I thought again of the crib scene. Would the wise men — and the wise women — arrive in time?

FIVE

Meeting needs

*The saying is sure and worthy of full
acceptance, that Christ Jesus came into
the world to save sinners.* (1 Tim 1:15)

COMPANIES which are in the business of selling
consumer goods of one kind or another increasingly
operate on an international basis. Which means
that advertising also has to be increasingly international. Over the last two or three years I had found
that more and more meetings with clients were
taking place abroad, as international companies
tried to find marketing solutions that would work
across national boundaries.

It was during January that I found myself travelling to Rome in the name of a catholic strategy for
Pronto Pizzas. That Rome should be the venue for
this particular meeting was something of an irony.
Whilst the imagery of the product was clearly linked
to Italy, the pizzas themselves were made in
Germany, and marketed throughout Europe on the
basis of a strategy led from the UK. Chris Mulligan
was therefore the key executive figure in defining
and carrying through a marketing solution for
Europe, and my agency was the lead agency in
developing the advertising as a major part of that
solution.

True to the international principles of this particular multinational company, however, the emerging
strategy was to be the result of European consulta-

tion across the markets in which Pronto Pizzas were now becoming established. The Pronto Pizza Committee (PPC) had been set up to develop such a strategy, and that objective was now being pursued through a series of monthly meetings, each of which was to be held in a different 'member country'. The first one, which took place just before Christmas, was in the UK. This one in Rome was the second in the series.

Janie, my assistant, and I had arrived in Rome very late on the evening before the meeting, and so we managed not to bump into any of the other delegates. Only when we turned up at the designated hotel conference room at eight-thirty the next morning did we see again the faces that were familiar from the last occasion in London. There were representatives from France, Germany, Holland, Spain and Denmark, as well as one marketing manager with responsibility for the emerging markets in Eastern Europe. Mulligan was there, of course, with his senior brand manager, Carol Clarkson.

The main item on the agenda concerned the development of the products themselves. The meeting in London had already dealt with the thorny issue of the pizza *base*. France had felt it to be too thick, and Holland had felt it to be too thin. Denmark had felt it to be too oily, and Spain had felt it to be too crisp. Those issues had now been put to one side pending a pan-European consumer test which would evaluate a number of alternative bases developed by the factory in Germany.

The base itself was not, therefore, a current issue. *That* debate would resume in two months' time on the basis of wide-ranging consumer evidence. What *was* an issue, however, was the range of pizza *toppings*.

As Pronto Pizzas had expanded across Europe, each country had selected its own favourite toppings, and so the total number of variations had multiplied to the point where only a few 'standard' recipes were being sold in more than one or two countries. Many of the other toppings were selling only in very small quantities, and consequently the factory efficiencies were suffering badly and costs were rising fast. Mulligan was therefore keen to get as much immediate agreement as possible on the rationalization of the current range and the development of new international recipes. Recipes that would appeal across a number of national boundaries, attracting new users whilst retaining the loyalty of those who already bought the brand.

The bulk of the morning was taken up with presentations from the various marketing managers, as each one set out the history and rationale for the range of toppings as they existed in his or her market. We then stopped briefly for a buffet lunch, and I prepared my slides for the presentation I was to give on the subject of 'Current US Trends in Pizzas' — which I had had prepared by the consumer planning division of our agency office in New York.

During the break for lunch I noticed that Carol Clarkson was called away to take a private telephone call in the hotel lobby. Carol was a petite woman in her late twenties with a striking smile and a very forceful character. I could see why she was able to hold her own when working for Chris Mulligan. It was impossible not to be aware of her presence at meetings, and so it was very obvious (to me at least) that she was not there when we recommenced after lunch. Mulligan looked uneasy, but told me to carry on, and so I stood up and began to make my presentation to the PPC.

I had gone through only the first few slides when the door opened and Carol entered with ashen cheeks and eyes that were puffy and red from crying. She sat down next to Mulligan and began whispering something in his ear. Unsure as to whether it would appear more rude to stop or to carry on, I brought my next slide up onto the screen. It was a brightly-coloured pie chart, and so I was able to step back from the table and wait, while the assembled group looked at the data.

After another minute or so of half-silence and sidelong glances, Carol stood up, tight-lipped, picked up her briefcase and left the room without a word. Mulligan was staring hard in front of him, his fingers bending a pencil to the point where it was about to snap. After what seemed an age, he looked up and made an effort to focus on the screen.

I took a deep breath, and stepped back towards the conference table, ready to continue with my presentation. As I began to speak, however, Mulligan held up his hand and stopped me.

'I ought to explain,' he said, falteringly. There was a brief silence. I don't think I had ever seen Mulligan lost for words before. 'I ought to explain,' he said again. 'Carol has had some bad news. Her boyfriend. That is, her ex-boyfriend. I mean to say, not her current one. That is, someone she has been very close to in the past. Well, he was killed in a road accident in London last night. And. Well, Carol is obviously very upset. She's going home on an earlier plane. So, we'll carry on without her. OK?'

Mulligan managed to inject a hint of his usual bluffness and aggression into the final 'OK'. Nobody said anything much, although Janie asked Mulligan if Carol would like someone to travel with her to the airport. Mulligan batted the question aside with a wave of his hand, and then, realizing that this might have appeared ungrateful, made a comment about Carol wanting to be alone.

All of which made his next remark rather surprising. As he had related the bald facts of Carol's bereavement I had felt strangely remote, as if trapped in amber. My heart felt called to intervene (if that is the word) in a situation of individual human distress. Yet my feet remained rooted to the spot — partly through the allegiance I felt I owed to the PPC as a whole, and partly through a desire not to appear intrusive. It was the first time I had felt such a dramatic tension of roles and responsibilities. I shifted uneasily, and coughed as a prelude to continuing my presentation.

'No, Michael,' said Mulligan abruptly. I stared back at him.

'Don't go on,' he continued. 'You're needed more elsewhere, I suspect. With your other hat on. Go on, Janie can do this.' He pointed at the screen. 'You go to Carol. Go on.'

I was about to make some comment back, but he had resumed his tough exterior and waved away my words before they had formed on my lips. Stopping only to pick up my jacket, I left the room to look for Carol.

I found her in the main hotel lobby, sitting alone on a large leather sofa. She smiled bravely when she saw me striding across the carpet towards her. My mind was racing and had still not caught up with the mix of emotions that were stirring my heart. How should I deal with this situation? What should I say? This was, after all, a woman that I only really knew professionally. Any relationship between us was on a business-only basis.

Fortunately I let my instincts lead me. I said nothing. I sat down next to her and folded her in my arms, and, as I did so, I felt her brave façade fall away as she allowed the real and hurt person to crumple with the pain of it all. Through her tears she tried to speak, but the words became lost, and I hung onto her, trying to let some of the hurt seep out of her and into me.

This did not seem to be ministry. This was not even consciously pastoral. This was surely nothing more than instinctive compassion. A simple acknowledgement of the pain that is stored up in the human condition. But it was all I could offer. All I could give. And I was myself touched and deeply moved by Carol's undemanding acceptance of me and my own impoverishment in the face of her suffering.

'There's nothing I can say really,' I murmured at last. 'Nothing that will make it hurt less.'

'I know,' she said through a tearful smile. 'Thank you for not saying anything.'

I thought back to the training weekend I had spent on bereavement counselling, but all I could think of were the little irregular sobs from the small body that I was holding close to my chest, and the fact that they seemed to be changing into more regular and deeper breaths.

After a few more minutes Carol freed herself from my embrace to blow her nose.

'I'm all right now,' she said, and I could see the

forceful side of her character struggling to resume some kind of control.

'No you're not,' I said, taking her hand. 'And don't think that you should be. "All right", that is. It's OK *not* to be "all right". We deal with these things. Yes. But we are changed by them too.'

I thought I might be saying too much, sounding too glib. But I kept going, conscious now that so long as I was speaking, Carol need say nothing.

'Not to be changed by them is to be less than fully human. You may think it's easy for me to talk like this.'

She moved her head slightly, not speaking.

'Well, perhaps it is,' I continued. 'But I honestly think that death is about transformation. You can take that to mean what you like. But I know — I *think* I know — that if the deaths of those close to us do not change us in some way, then we were never really part of a common life in the first place.'

I could hear the rational and critical part of me beginning to take issue with the words that were being formed by my intuitive voice. I would risk one more comment.

'When you get home, don't be alone, Carol. Try to be with those others who will also be sharing the loss and feeling the pain. If for no other reason than that they may need your strength.'

I shut up as Carol put her arms around me. It was almost as if she were ministering to *my* need — as a minister. As if she were finding some strength in being able to comfort the poor, confused pastor. When the taxi arrived to take her to the airport she was still holding me as she told me about Dan — how they had lived together for two years, and how they had split up six months before. And when she had gone, how did I feel? Saddened? Weary? No. I felt privileged. A strange and somewhat egocentric reaction, perhaps. But that is how I felt, and before returning to the meeting, I thanked God for the time I'd been able to spend with Carol.

As I went back into the meeting room all the faces turned to look at me.

'Carol's just left for the airport,' I said.

Mulligan nodded and then immediately proceeded to make a point about the projected capacity for frozen pizzas over the next two years. I resumed my seat and the meeting carried on for another two hours, at the end of which time the group had agreed on a core range of six toppings which would form the basis for a progressive harmonization of products across all markets over a period of eighteen months.

When the day-long conference ended, Mulligan seemed noticeably pleased with himself and the result. I could still remember, however, how unlike himself he had looked when explaining Carol's situation earlier in the day. I felt that perhaps this had been a glimpse of a more obviously sensitive man, and I wanted to thank him for giving me permission, as it were, to be with Carol.

We were booked on the same flight back to London, and so we travelled back to the airport together. When we arrived there, Janie went off to do some duty-free shopping and Mulligan and I headed to the bar for a drink.

'I wanted to say "thank you",' I said.

'What for?'

'For releasing me from the meeting so that I could be with Carol. That was very thoughtful of you.'

'Oh.' Mulligan looked slightly abstracted. 'Oh,

that. Hell, that was nothing. I could see she needed you more than I did. I suppose that's what you're there for, isn't it? After all, you did once tell me that you were a priest *all* the time. Not just on Sundays. Well, I mean . . . *You* would have known what to say.'

I smiled, taking a long draught from my tall glass of lager.

'As it happens,' I said, 'I didn't say very much at all. I don't think there *is* much you can say when it comes to it.'

Mulligan's brow furrowed. He lit a cigarette.

'What did Carol say?' he said, after inhaling the smoke. 'Did she say much?'

'No,' I replied, conscious that anything said to me was in strict confidence. 'No, she didn't say much.'

I fell silent, not wishing to be drawn on the subject. Mulligan was fiddling nervously with his cigarette packet. His empty eyes were looking past me at something, or nothing, in the distance.

'I slept with her, you know,' he said quietly.

'I'm sorry,' I said, meaning that I wasn't sure that I had heard him properly.

'I slept with her,' he said again bitterly. 'With Carol.'

And then, in response to my wide-eyed look:

'Last night. I slept with Carol last night. At the hotel.'

He was waiting for me to say something.

'Are you having a relationship with her?'

'What the hell's *that* supposed to mean? Look, Michael, it wasn't the first time, if that's what you're getting at. The first time was several months ago.'

'About the time . . . '

'*After* that. After she split up with whatever his name was.'

I was silent again, but it was clear that Mulligan

seemed to want me to make the running. As if he felt he deserved some kind of interrogation.

'And your wife?' I felt on dodgy ground. I had never met Mrs Mulligan, but I knew there were two children.

Mulligan stubbed out what remained of his cigarette and quickly lit another one. The usual aggression seemed to be draining out of him, to be replaced by a deep sadness.

'Things haven't been right between us for a while. Since before . . . Well, you know. She probably knows that I'm . . .' He stopped to draw on his cigarette. 'Unfaithful. That's the word, isn't it. Unfaithful. Hah!' He laughed a bitter laugh. 'So what is it to be *faithful*, eh? Tell me that, Reverend! What is it to be faithful?'

I felt that he had more to say, and so I decided to risk being direct.

'You tell *me*, Chris. What *is* it to be faithful, do you think?'

He drank the remainder of his lager in one go.

'I don't know, Michael. God, I don't know. Except . . .'

'Yes?'

'I think Carol still loved her old boyfriend. And he's dead. And, Christ, I don't know, but somehow his dying made last night seem so . . . so . . . nothing. If he hadn't died, I would probably have gone home thinking that I'd had a good time. But instead, I feel . . . cheap. Unloved, for God's sake. Can you believe that? Chris Mulligan worried that nobody loves him! This guy's dead, and I'm alive, and I'm the one that's worried! Can you believe that!'

He slumped back in the chair, grinding his teeth together.

'I can believe that,' I said softly, for I could see Janie coming back towards us. 'Look. Here's my personal card. My number at home. Give me a ring there if ever you want to talk.'

Mulligan slipped the card into his pocket silently.

'So, who's for another one?' said Janie, spying our empty glasses as she approached the table.

'Yes please, my love,' said Mulligan, leaning forward with a mischievous grin fixed like a mask on his broad face.

* * *

The St John's and St Mary's joint Parochial Church Council (PCC) met every eight weeks. Those meetings which occurred during the winter months were purposely arranged, I feel sure, so that they fell upon the coldest and wettest evenings of the year. Whatever else they may have been, PCC meetings were great tests of Christian commitment.

It was expected that I, as a member of the clergy team, should attend these meetings. I made a point, however, of trying to keep a fairly low profile in the vain hope that matters to do with the replacement of guttering or the purchase of a new light fitting for one of the church porches might pass me by. Alas, there was no escape from the discussions of the devoted body of worthies who dedicated their lives to the maintenance of the church fabric, and (despite my best efforts) I found myself lobbied enthusiastically by everyone with a pet parochial project.

On this particular winter's evening we were huddled in the chill air of St Mary's hall to discuss the structure of the church. Not, I hasten to add, the *organizational* structure of the church (either locally

or, indeed, nationally), but rather the material structure of St Marys — from flagstones to steeple, and everything in between.

I tied my scarf securely round my neck as Hilary Noble began her statement on the subject. Hilary was a somewhat prim lady who, whilst being only thirty years old, always gave the impression of having (as they say) many more miles on the clock. Her career as a local solicitor made her, in lots of ways, an admirable choice as parish secretary. The legalistic way in which she viewed *every* issue to do with the church was, however, something of a mixed blessing.

'Mr Chairman, members of the PCC, with reference to item three of the agenda, pertaining to the aforementioned structure of St Mary's church, I would like to draw members' attention to Exhibit 2, being the report of the diocesan surveyor in respect of the review instigated by this committee pursuant to the regrettable incident referred to in the minutes of the meeting of 28th September.'

'What the blazes is she talking about?' I whispered in the ear of Stephen Pickle, the full-time curate of the parish, and priest-in-charge at St John's. Stephen was a long, thin thirty-year-old, with a mop of ginger hair, and a very pleasant sense of irreverence.

'Damned if I know,' said Stephen, with a characteristic curl of the lip. 'What do you think *this* is? "Shooting dice to play the game is rubbish." Four letters. Third one is A.'

I nodded supportively at Hilary Noble whilst thinking about Stephen's crossword clue.

'Crap,' I said at last.

'Pardon?' said Stephen.

'Crap,' I said again. 'That's your word. A game in which you shoot dice is called "crap". And as you well know, the word is also used colloquially to mean "rubbish".'

'Thanks,' said Stephen. Then, after a pause, 'Put your hand up.'

'Why? What are we voting for?'

'I've no idea. But everyone else seems to be in favour.'

Stephen and I found ourselves voting in favour of going directly to Section III 4(b)ii of the report – which seemed to be a good move because it meant that Hilary Noble sat down and Frank Foster stood up.

Frank, one of the churchwardens of St Mary's, was a very different animal to Hilary in that he spoke English and so could be understood for most of the time. He gazed around at his peers, his ruddy face exuding good sense. Frank was a retired tax inspector, but looked as if he should have been a farmer at some stage in his life. In his tweed jacket and woollen tie he looked every inch the countryman.

'I'll come straight to the point,' he said. 'The fact is, we've got a big problem. There is *some* good news. And the good news is that, for once, it's not the roof. The roof's OK. Topping, I might say.'

Frank raised his monumentally hairy eyebrows and grinned threateningly at the assembled faces, pleased at his little pun.

'The *bad* news is that the foundations are dodgy. Or at least that's the interpretation that I put on a lot of complicated gumf in the surveyor's report. Now, before you all start panicking, I've got to say that the church isn't exactly falling down. Well, not yet, at least. But the outlook isn't good.'

You could have heard a pin drop in the hall. Apocalypses might come and go, but the idea of St Mary's falling down was enough to get the undivided attention of everyone on the PCC.

'Oh dear,' said Stephen under his breath.

I turned to look at my colleague, who was rubbing his hand across his long chin in a worried way.

'It may not be as bad as all that,' I said, trying to sound encouraging.

'Oh, but it is,' replied Stephen. 'Unless I can get seventeen across, I've no chance of completing twelve down. It must be an anagram.'

I looked at the jumble of letters that he had scribbled in the margin, and then turned back towards Frank.

'It's all to do with earth movements of one kind or another. Subsidence, basically. Not to put too fine a point on it, St Mary's is going downhill.'

The hawkish grin was once more displayed to the assembled company, but the PCC was no longer in the mood for Frank's puns.

'That is to say,' said Frank, gamely continuing through the taut silence, 'the church is slowly moving down the hill. It's only been a couple of inches over the last year, but if things carry on in this way, the surveyor's report indicates that St Mary's is likely to collide with Sainsbury's within the next two hundred years.'

Stephen had put down his crossword, unable to unscramble the letters of the clue.

'It's that prayer you did at the evening service last week,' he whispered.

'What prayer?'

'Don't you remember? You prayed that the Holy Spirit would move the church on. Well, there you are. He's obviously decided to move it on down the hill.'

I laughed involuntarily, and then tried desperately to make it look as if I were coughing. I must have made a fairly good job of it, because Lynda Soames turned round to offer me a Fisherman's Friend. I looked at the packet warily.

'It'll get rid of it,' Lynda said with that air of absolute confidence that, somehow, only evangelicals ever manage to attain.

'Get rid of it?' I croaked, still maintaining the pretence of some oesophageal irritation.

'The cough,' she said. 'They get rid of most things. Hiccups. Wind. Bad breath. Try one.'

I thanked her and helped myself to a small brown lozenge.

During this brief interlude, the subject of the

subsiding church had progressed, and members of the PCC were asking Frank questions related to the surveyor's report. As my mind focused once more on the proceedings, somebody was asking whether the whole church was moving together, or whether some parts were moving more than others.

Stephen (who was always likely to see the funny side of *any* situation) had stuffed a handkerchief in his mouth to stop himself from laughing out loud, and his cheeks were beginning to turn pink. Frank Foster was not sure how to answer the point that had been raised, and so referred the questioner to the main report which could be consulted after the meeting. Already, however, a picture had been created in my mind of the church moving down the hill at different speeds. The nave racing ahead towards its meeting with Sainsbury's, and the chancel hanging back, reluctant to leave its customary position at the top of the hill.

Mary Brown, the parish's most glamorous granny, had just risen to pledge the support of the Mother's Union for any structural work that had to be undertaken on the church building, when the door of the hall opened and Malcolm Potts burst in with a wide smile spread across his broad white face. Malcolm was the organist at St Mary's, when he wasn't teaching music at a local secondary school or spotting trains at Clapham Junction.

He pulled himself out of a long scarf which had been wound round his neck three times, threw off his anorak with an air of gay abandon, and pushed his heavy-rimmed spectacles back up his long nose.

'Begging your pardon for the interruption, Mr Chairman,' he said nodding energetically at Canon George. 'But I've just received some very good news about the church, and I thought everyone would want to hear it at once.'

'We certainly will if it's anything to do with St Mary's moving back up the hill,' said Frank Foster, grinning.

Malcolm looked perplexed. He usually understood Frank's little puns and allusions, but this one passed him by completely.

'Go on, Malcolm,' said Canon George, his face a picture of serene hopefulness. 'What's this good news then?'

'Well,' said the organist, wringing his hands together with delight. 'It's about the repairs to the organ. The cost isn't going to be as much as I'd feared.' He nodded wildly at all the upturned faces.

'Carry on, Malcolm,' said Canon George again when it became clear that Malcolm could have gone on nodding for some time.

'Only half as much, in fact,' continued Malcolm. 'Which means that it will only cost us fifteen thousand pounds.'

There was a short stark silence, and then Stephen almost spat in my ear as he gave his reaction to this piece of 'good news'.

'What the . . . ! Only fifteen thousand! We've got a church on the move, and Malcolm wants us to find fifteen thousand pounds to repair the organ!'

'Well, *you're* all right,' I said.

'What do you mean, I'm all right?'

'St John's isn't moving down any hills, and your organ's functioning perfectly well.'

'You leave my organ out of it,' said Stephen. 'And, anyway, the only reason St John's is not moving down a hill is because there's no hill for it to move down. Don't forget, we haven't had a surveyor's report on St John's yet. When we *do* have one, I wouldn't mind betting that the place is sinking into some hitherto undetected marshy bog at the end of the High Street.'

All around us members of the PCC were hunched together in whispering huddles. Only a very few of them had had any idea that the church organ was in need of any attention. Certainly only one or two knew that an original estimate had put the cost at almost thirty thousand pounds.

And so it was that Malcolm's news, far from seeming 'good' to the assembled company, actually sounded like something of a death knell after the revelation of the subsiding church building.

Canon George coughed firmly but diplomatically and tried to regain some kind of order in the church hall.

'Ladies. Gentlemen. Please. There is no cause for immediate alarm . . .'

Stephen whispered in my ear that this simply meant that we would all panic later over a stiff drink in the vicarage.

'Really, ladies and gentlemen,' persevered Canon George. 'Could we *please* come to order?'

He had hardly raised his voice, but almost immediately the murmur of voices ceased and all eyes were turned towards the meeting's chairman.

'Thank you,' said Canon George, smiling graciously. 'Now I know that for some of you this piece of, er, "good" news may have came as something of a shock. But let me say at once that we must try to keep all these matters in perspective. The organ is not the pivotal point of our coming together as a worshipping community.'

'I'm afraid I beg to differ, Mr Chairman,' said Doreen Butcher firmly. 'That organ has been part of my life for more than twenty-five years. If the organ's allowed to die, then it'll be like tearing the heart of the church out.'

Stephen muttered something that I didn't quite catch, although it didn't sound particularly Christian.

'No one's suggesting that we will allow the organ to die, Doreen,' said Canon George, still managing to sound like the most good-humoured man on this earth. 'After all, as you implied yourself, Doreen, what we're talking about here is the church's vital organ.' Canon George smiled his smile of jovial innocence, and everyone else groaned.

'But can I please remind everybody that we should not be discussing the organ at this point. May I in fact remind you all that we are still on item three of the agenda, "Surveyor's Report on St Mary's".'

Be that as it may, Malcolm had already begun to pass around colour photographs of bits of the internal workings of the organ. Most people gazed at them with total incomprehension, feeling that a close-up of one piece of pipe was pretty much like the close-up of another piece of pipe. Some enquiring members turned the photographs over in the hope that there would be some indication of which way up the picture was supposed to be. But all were agreed on the fact that it was the least interesting set of photographs that anyone had ever seen.

All of which helped to dampen the enthusiasm with which a few individuals had leapt into the debate about the organ. The photographs were passed back fairly quickly to Malcolm, with a few souls brave enough to venture noncommittal comments like 'Indeed' and 'Fascinating'.

'Thank you,' said Canon George at last, with an audible sigh, as the hubbub died down and Malcolm took a seat at the back of the hall. '*Now*, ladies and gentlemen, if we could please get back to the matter in hand, which is the structure of St Mary's.'

A hand went up in the front row.

'Yes, Christine,' said Canon George patiently.

Christine was, like Hilary and many of the other PCC members, a regular worshipper at St John's rather than at St Mary's. She was known as something of a 'mystic' by those who knew her, and as something of a misfit by those who didn't.

'Can I please ask, Mr Chairman, how long we're likely to be on this item? Because item 6, "The Spiritual and Pastoral Needs of the Parish" has already been held over for two meetings, and at the rate we're going tonight, it will have to be held over again.'

'Thank you, Christine,' said Canon George, adopting his most sympathetic expression as he looked back at Christine in her politically correct T-shirt and psychedelic leggings. 'I understand your concerns, and do, of course, share them. I hope the meeting will note them as well, and help me to move the business of the evening on at a respectable pace. But I know that many here would not wish things to go on past ten o'clock, and so, I am afraid, we may have to face the possibility that the spiritual and pastoral needs of the parish will once more have to be held over.'

'Well, there's a surprise,' said Stephen, who was gazing abstractedly at the ceiling.

'So,' said Canon George, trying to summon up his most authoritative manner. 'If we could please return to the matter in hand. I think we had reached the point where the church was going downhill. Now, was there anything else you wished to say, Frank?'

Of course there was. Frank stood up again and carried on where he had left off.

Stephen returned to his crossword.

I tried to concentrate first on what Frank was saying, and then on the infuriating anagram, but my mind kept filling up with thoughts of Chris Mulligan, Pronto Pizzas, and what it meant to be faithful.

SIX

Crossing over

For in the one Spirit we were all baptized into one body — Jews or Greeks, slaves or free. (1 Corinthians 12:13)

WE HAD been having an evening clergy staff meeting in the vicarage study. Canon George and Stephen Pickle were both wearing their cassocks, and I was dressed in a T-shirt and a pair of jeans.

'So, Michael,' said Canon George, chewing on his strong coffee in a meditative fashion. 'What else do we need to bring you up to speed on?'

He looked at Stephen over the top of his glasses.

'Funerals,' said Stephen without a moment's hesitation.

Canon George pushed out his bottom lip and waggled his head about sagely.

'Yes,' he said. 'Funerals. You probably won't do many, not being around during the day. But you ought to be ready. You never know when you're going to need to do one. Best be ready.'

I was suddenly seized with a feeling of indeterminate panic. I could be walking home this very night, I thought, and find myself faced with the pressing need to do a funeral. At least I wasn't wearing my dog collar, I reflected. Surely that would mean that people were less likely to come up to me in the street and demand that I came away immediately to do a funeral somewhere close by.

Canon George seemed not to have noticed my slightly abstracted air.

'Yes, you never know,' he continued. 'You never know. It could be family, or a friend — but, almost certainly, you will be asked to do a funeral sooner rather than later.'

I nodded in agreement and the meeting ended with the suggestion that I should try to get along to one of the funerals being conducted by either Canon George or Stephen as soon as possible. Once I had observed one or both of my colleagues in action, it would be appropriate (we decided) for me to be shown exactly what was required in terms of both the service itself, and the important matters of dealing with the family, the funeral directors, the cemetery superintendents, and so on.

If there was one thing that was already becoming apparent through my ministry, it was that God has a pronounced sense of humour. Soon after I arrived home there was a knock at the door. When I went to see who it was I found Martha Cummings standing with a bottle of milk in either hand. Martha, a lady in her late sixties, lived just across the way at number twenty-four.

'Your milk,' she declared, thrusting into my face the bottles which Cheryl and I had forgotten to bring in that morning. 'I was going to apologize for calling so late. But now I don't feel so bad.'

I looked at her blankly.

'Well, if I *hadn't* called,' she continued, 'you wouldn't have had your milk, would you?'

'Quite,' I replied as I tried to understand what was going on. One thing was clear. Martha had not called merely to ensure that our calcium intakes were being maintained at a healthy level. I decided to invite her in for a cup of tea.

'I'll come straight to the point,' she said after several minutes of unstoppable chatter, during which time I had made, brewed and poured the tea. 'I won't beat about the bush,' she said, gulping back the hot liquid with her asbestos mouth. 'Dad's gone at last.'

I was somewhat nonplussed. I offered her a digestive biscuit.

'Gone where?' I asked, trying to look understanding.

'Gone,' she repeated. 'Crossed over. Died. Dead. Passed away.'

At a moment of intense pastoral need, my mind was suddenly filled with an image of the dead parrot sketch from 'Monty Python's Flying Circus'.

'Oh,' I murmured, employing the utmost muscular skill in keeping the smile off my face. 'I'm sorry.'

'No need to be sorry, Michael,' said Martha. 'He was ninety-eight, and he died with a smile on his face.'

'Indeed?'

'He was in the hospital, you see. One of the nurses bent over his bed, and he pinched her bottom and died.'

'Ah,' I again murmured, not sure of what my reaction should be.

'Anyway, Michael, as I say, to get straight to the point,' said Martha again, this time spraying the carpet with digestive crumbs. 'Can you do the funeral?'

A nervous and slightly hysterical chuckle started in my throat, but very quickly transformed itself into a cough and a splutter.

'Why, of course,' I said. 'Of course I will, Martha.' I smiled broadly at her in a way I judged to be supportive, and added, 'I don't get a chance to do too many funerals, you know.'

'That's good then,' she said, draining the last dregs of the tea. 'There's just one thing though. He's going to be buried in a Roman Catholic cemetery. Is that still all right?'

'Was your Dad a Catholic, then, Martha?'

'No. He said he was a Methodist. But he wasn't anything really.'

'So why the Catholic funeral?'

'Mum was a Catholic, and she's already there.'

'Right,' I ventured, while my mind raced from one thought to another. So why do I, an Anglican deacon, have to get a Methodist who wants a Catholic funeral? Am I allowed to do it? Where will it be? What sort of service will they expect?

I tried to put all my worries to one side and to respond to Martha's need.

'Right, Martha. You leave it to me. I'll talk to my vicar and find out what the situation is, and then I'll come round and let you know how we take it on from here. By the way, what was your Dad's name?'

'His real name was Archibald Leonard, but he was always called "Nobby". Nobby Stride. Quite fitting really.'

I decided not to ask why, and contented myself with adopting an expression of deep understanding.

'Do you have a big family, Martha?' I asked. 'Will there be many people going to the funeral?'

'I wouldn't have thought so,' she said. 'My only sister died when she was little. There are a couple of cousins. That's all.'

'And what about you, Martha? How will you get there? Will you be all right?'

'Oh, don't worry about me. Maria's taking me.'

'Maria?'

'My lodger,' said Martha. 'Haven't you met Maria?'

I suddenly recalled having seen a very attractive young woman going in and out of Martha's house recently.

'Maria's pregnant,' added Martha quickly, as if by way of warning. 'But she's still got two months or so to go. So she said she could take me in her Beetle.'

'Her Beetle,' I echoed.

'Yes,' continued Martha. 'It's a car.'

'I know,' I said flatly. It seemed about time to end the conversation. 'Right then, Martha, as I said, I'll speak to the vicar and get back to you.'

My speech was clear but my head was filling with images of Beetles and babies. Something told me this was not going to be as straightforward as I would have hoped.

* * *

I rang Canon George the next morning. He was quite clear about the situation. First of all, he had never heard of a Roman Catholic cemetery in thirty years of being a priest. He felt sure that the cemetery in question would be the usual interdenominational and municipal setup. Which meant that the only real issues were the views of Martha and the cousins. What were *their* expectations? Were they churchgoers and did they expect any particular kind of funeral? If they didn't, then the way seemed clear for me to do my 'maiden' service. I should therefore get back in touch with Martha, find out what the expectations of the family were, and then tell her that the funeral directors should get in touch with me to arrange the practicalities.

When that had been done, Canon George would school me in how to handle the situation and the relatives, and would also, of course, take me through the service so that I knew what I was doing.

Martha was very matter-of-fact when I spoke to her about the family's expectations. No, there wouldn't be more than a handful attending the funeral. No, none of them was religious in any way. No, they didn't mind what I did, so long as Dad got a proper send off. On that basis I asked Martha to let the funeral directors have my name and telephone number, and I sat back to wait for the next thing to happen.

I didn't have long to wait. The next day the phone rang and I picked up the receiver to hear a voice asking for Father Dunn. This wasn't the time, I judged, to discourage further use of the title 'Father', and so I simply said, 'Yes. Speaking.'

Over the next few minutes the man at the other end of the line enquired whether or not I had agreed to officiate at the funeral of the late Archibald Leonard Stride, told me the time proposed for the funeral, and asked if that would be convenient. The time suggested was lunchtime on the Friday of the following week. I looked in the diary and calculated that I could be free on that day if I could manage to rearrange the continuing saga of 'Macro-Suds'. I scribbled a quick note to myself and agreed to the proposal.

On enquiring about the cemetery, I was told that it was on the other side of London. The funeral directors would send me a card telling me the name of it and how to get there. The man on the other end of the phone then came to the subject of the fee.

'We usually give our priests £40. Would that figure be acceptable to you, Father?'

I was very briefly lost for something to say. I had forgotten that there was any fee involved. Faced with this question, I suddenly found that my chief concern was not to give away the fact that I was as yet still a deacon, and that this was, as it were, 'my first time'. I cleared my throat and tried to sound as if such mere details were slightly tiresome.

'Oh, yes,' I said. 'Yes, of course. If that's what you *normally* do . . . Yes, I'm sure £40 will be most . . .'

My words drifted away into something of a gurgle, and I tried to extricate myself from the conversation before any more damage could be done. On the one hand I was aware that £40 would in no real sense compensate for what would essentially be a day's 'lost' holiday. And on the other hand, I was acutely conscious that it seemed a lot of money to pay someone who hadn't a notion of what he was supposed to be doing.

* * *

The next day was a Saturday and Canon George and I had arranged to meet so that he could begin to prepare me for the forthcoming ordeal. The morning post had brought the expected card from the funeral directors:

Re. funeral of Archibald Leonard Stride
at the cemetery of Saint Ignatius.

The card had started a little alarm bell ringing inside my head. The cemetery of Saint Ignatius did not sound like 'an interdenominational and municipal setup', and so it was the first thing I mentioned as Canon George and I sat down in his study.

'Yes, I see what you mean,' he said, sitting down heavily at his desk. 'But I still say that in thirty years as a priest I have never come across a Roman Catholic cemetery. Still, I'm always willing to admit that I might be wrong. You'd better ring the funeral directors, Michael.'

I picked up the phone in the vicarage study.

'Ah, hello. My name is Michael Dunn. Yes. I'm doing the funeral of Archibald Stride next Friday. Yes. Now, could I clarify one thing, please. Do you think I'm a Roman Catholic? Ah. Oh. Ah. Right. Right.'

When I had replaced the receiver Canon George and I looked at each other across the desk.

'Well,' I said. 'The cemetery is a Roman Catholic cemetery. They only deal in Roman Catholic funerals. And they think that I'm a Roman Catholic priest. Apart from that, everything's hunky dory.' I think I may have giggled nervously at this point.

There then followed a brief interlude during which Canon George first told me how 'you learn something new every day', and then went on to suggest that, in a manner of speaking, 'we were all baptized into one body — Anglicans, Methodists and Roman Catholics.' It therefore didn't really matter that I was, as it were, crossing over into new territory. We were all children of God, after all, when everything was said and done.

When it was clear, however, that I did not look reassured by this generous ecumenical spirit, he recommended that I should immediately follow the advice that the funeral director had given me and phone the cemetery superintendent at St Ignatius's.

The phone was answered by the superintendent's wife. As the superintendent was not due back for a little while, I decided that I would put his wife in the picture. When I told her that I was not, in fact, a Roman Catholic, her response was less than consoling.

'Oh dear. Oh dear. Oh dear. Oh dear, oh dear, oh dear.'

This did not, as you might imagine, fill me with confidence. In fact, it did quite the reverse and made me start wondering why I had ever wanted to be a clergyman in the first place. As my whole life began to pass before me, I managed to pull myself together and asked her what she thought I should do.

After a few more 'Oh dear's she said that she thought that her husband had better be the one to give an opinion. I therefore asked her to get him to phone me and I gave her two phone numbers at which I could be reached.

The first number, I said, is my home number where I shall be for the most of the afternoon. The second number is the number of the vicarage, where I am at the moment.

Unfortunately what I had assumed to be a fairly straightforward piece of information only served to draw forth another string of 'Oh dear's — brought on by the poor unfortunate woman's confusion about what I was trying to say.

'I'm sorry, Father,' she said at last. 'But I'm confused again. You've given me a phone number for your home, and a different one for the vicarage. Don't you live with the vicar then, if you're the curate?'

I took a deep breath and spoke very slowly into the mouthpiece.

'I live at my home with my *wife* and my *daughter*. The vicar lives at the vicarage with his *wife* and his *children*.'

I heard what I thought were embarrassed giggles at the end of the line, but they might have been sobs.

'Oh dear,' said the superintendent's wife. 'Silly me. Of course. You do things differently, don't you?'

I was somewhat relieved when the conversation ended, although still hanging over me like the sword of Damocles was the prospect of talking to the superintendent himself.

It was some hours later when that discussion took place. The cemetery superintendent revealed himself to be a bluff man who gave the impression of not being easily ruffled, and who was not likely to take a dogmatic line on anything if there was room for compromise. He explained to me that, as far as he was concerned, I could be the Archbishop of Canterbury. He had had 'all sorts' in his cemetery, and the thought of an Anglican burying a Methodist was neither here nor there.

I decided to take comfort from this, although, if anything, it made me more keenly aware of some of the absurdities that surround so-called 'organized' religions.

The next step in what was fast becoming a ludicrous initiation to the funeral rite, was my introduction to the service itself. The general feeling between Canon George and Stephen was that the service should, in some ways, respect the fact that the funeral was at least nominally Roman Catholic. Canon George took me through the 'old' Catholic funeral rite, offering suggestions about how various bits of Anglican prayer could be included as well. Stephen, who was clearly more conversant with current Catholic practices, gave me a copy of the 'new' Roman funeral rite, marked up with the bits he thought I should include. All this 'help' only served to add to my state of confusion and slight desperation.

That night I settled myself down with a strong drink and the various rites, determined to concoct something that would keep everyone reasonably happy. I decided that if the members of the deceased's family were not churchgoers, they were unlikely to want to join in a lot of responses. In fact, I felt that they might well be intimidated by having to follow anything in a book, and so I resolved that I would design my own service to suit the occasion.

Nobby Stride was to be buried rather than cremated, and so I was aware that I had to conduct part of the service in the chapel at the cemetery, and part of it at the graveside.

As a last bit of preparation, however, I knew that Stephen was conducting a funeral service on the Tuesday before my ordeal, and so I decided that I would take off yet more time from work so as to attend as an observer. This was to be a cremation, but I felt that some of the principles of conduct would still apply.

* * *

I arrived at the local 'crem' early, wearing my dog collar lest I be thought of as a gate-crasher. Stephen was standing in the doorway waiting for me, and soon I was being introduced to the superintendent, the gravediggers, and the man who organized the music. Stephen showed me around inside the chapel, and I took especial note of the two buttons on the lectern. One for letting the funeral directors know that the service had ended, and one for consigning the coffin to be cremated.

'Whatever you do, don't get them mixed up!' said Stephen.

In this particular crem the second button started the process whereby the coffin would descend by means of hydraulics, disappearing from the view of those gathered in the chapel. Stephen told me a story of how one minister had accidentally pressed the wrong button at the wrong time, consigning a candidate for burial towards a fiery end only minutes into the service. Fortunately the coffin was not committed to the flames, but then the hydraulic system was not capable of lifting its load back into position, and so the service had to continue with the deceased out of sight halfway down the shaft.

'So, remember to make sure you know which button is which when you get to St Ignatius's,' Stephen said once more.

At this point we were alerted to the fact that the funeral cortege was approaching the chapel, and I took up a position at the back. The next twenty minutes or so went very quickly, and almost before I knew what was happening it was all over. All in all it had been a very uneventful occasion, although I was very interested to notice the degree to which Stephen had departed from 'the text'. If nothing else, this reassured me that my efforts of the previous night to construct a 'customized' service probably fell within the bounds of what one might call pastoral sensitivity.

When the mourners had departed, Stephen gave

me a confidential wink and lent me his clerical cloak (lined with red silk) which he said I might need, to keep off the elements.

At home, later that day, I tried on the cloak and found that it made me look rather more like Count Dracula than a Roman Catholic priest. On which subject there was still one thing that I had to get clear with Canon George.

I phoned him to ask if I should wear my stole deacon-style (that is, diagonally and tied at the side, rather than hanging straight down as a priest would do). His response was that, given I was doing a Roman funeral in a Roman cemetery, this was really something of a side issue. He suggested I went for the full impersonation, wearing my stole as if I were already a priest.

In for a penny, in for a pound, as they say.

* * *

Friday morning arrived, and it was raining cats and dogs. I decided that my impersonation of a Roman Catholic priest must be done as well as I could manage, so I put on my best formal clerical shirt (the one with the very narrow opening), and a black suit.

I was just about to go to the toilet for the third time when the doorbell rang. Martha was standing there, beaming at me and looking unashamedly relaxed and happy.

'Right, then,' she said. 'I'll see you there, then.'

'See you there, then,' I echoed, in a way that implied it was all in a day's work.

Fifteen minutes later I was checking (for the umpteenth time) that I had put cassock, cotta, stole and cloak in the boot of the car. I hauled myself into the driving seat, set out the street map on the passenger seat and, sending up a quick arrow prayer, headed off on my journey to cross over to the other side of London.

The traffic was heavy that day and I had opted to go through the City. It was just as well that I had left plenty of time because I arrived at the cemetery of St Ignatius a full two hours later. It was ten minutes past noon when I drove warily through the wrought iron gates. The funeral was due to begin at one o'clock.

'Good day to you, Father,' said the rosy-faced woman behind the counter as I entered what looked to be a front office. 'I'll be with you in just a minute.'

I looked at my shoes self-consciously and then nodded at an elderly couple who were huddled in a corner of the room. The rosy-faced woman came back in.

'Now, Father, what can I be doing for you?'

'I'm . . .' I coughed. 'I'm Father Dunn,' I said. 'Here for the funeral of Nobby, that is, Archibald Stride.'

'Mr Stride,' said the woman with what appeared to be a certain amount of relish. 'Oh, Father Dunn!' she exclaimed suddenly, her face lighting up even more. 'The Anglican!'

I must have looked very embarrassed.

'Er, yes,' I muttered, trying not to look at the elderly couple whom I felt sure must be reacting with horror. An Anglican! And in *here*!

The cemetery superintendent's wife (for, indeed, the rosy-faced woman was none other than she) now seemed not at all put out by this knowledge. In fact, she laughed heartily, throwing back her head and showing off her chest to good advantage.

'Oh dear, oh dear. John and I had a good laugh about that,' she said. 'I bet you did as well, didn't you?'

'Yes,' I said in a dull, flat voice. 'I had a good laugh about it.'

I was suddenly aware of the sound of the elderly couple breathing.

'Mind you,' said the superintendent's wife. 'You *do* look like one.'

'Oh, do I?' I said.

'Oh dear me yes. Doesn't he look like one?' she said, over my shoulder, to the elderly couple in the corner.

'*What* does he look like?' croaked the old woman, her words rattling around in the lower reaches of her throat.

'A *real* priest,' shouted the superintendent's wife. 'He looks like a *real* priest.'

'He looks like a priest all right,' said the old woman smiling bleakly.

I looked back at the rosy-faced woman who had fixed me with a penetrating stare.

'You're early, you know,' she said.

'I know,' I said.

Once again I felt my innocence betraying itself. The way she had said it implied that any normal priest would have arrived only minutes before the due time. Yet here I was, a full three-quarters of an hour before the service.

'Perhaps I could wait in the vestry. I mean the sacristy,' I said, correcting myself to use the more Catholic term.

The superintendent's wife nodded but was looking at the elderly couple in a coquettish way.

'He's married, you know,' she said. 'Got a kid.'

I noticed a look of distinct anguish pass over the face of the old man, but was not sure whether it was horror or sympathy.

I stumbled through a doorway on my left and into the sacristy of the chapel which adjoined the front office. The whole building was somewhat dilapidated and looked not to be used very much. It was clear that most of the Roman Catholic funerals were conducted at the local churches, with only the graveside bits being done 'on site'.

I hung up my robes and went to look at the chapel itself. It was rather like a disused barn – large, empty, cold and damp. Nothing at all like the crem that I had visited three days before. There was a crude lectern pushed to one side from where I would presumably lead the service. But no electrics at all, and no buttons to confuse me. All in all, the place seemed to be untouched by modernity.

I was just beginning to feel slightly despondent when I heard a bluff voice behind me.

'Good day, Father. Are you all right there? Or will you be needing anything?'

It was the voice of the superintendent, and I shook his hand as warmly as if he had been an old mate.

'Good day,' I echoed. 'Thank you. Yes. Everything's fine. Just fine. Perhaps you could light the candles, please?'

While the superintendent was sorting out the candles, I changed into my cassock and had a last look at my notes. It was about twenty-five minutes to one when the man from the funeral directors came and introduced himself. I managed to stop myself from exclaiming, 'What are you doing here!

It's not supposed to happen until one o'clock!' Instead I tried to look blissfully calm. Serene even. Just as I imagined Canon George would have done in the same situation.

It so happened that the funeral cortege had 'made excellent time' crossing London and was there, now, outside, waiting.

'Any time you're ready, Father,' said the stoutly-built young man who looked like dependability incarnate. He pushed a brown envelope into my hand and gave me a knowing look.

I stuffed the funeral fee into my cassock pocket and fought to maintain my calm demeanour.

'The buttons,' I stammered. 'There are no buttons. That is, I'm used to having some buttons to push. How will you know when I've finished?'

'Oh, yes, sir. Bit basic here, isn't it? You'll just have to open the side door. Up there, in front of the pews. We'll be waiting just outside. We'll come in, pick up the coffin, and then you and I will lead the way to the graveside. It's not far, sir. Just a short walk.'

His smile gave me a much needed feeling of renewed confidence.

'Now, the mourners are just looking at the flowers at the moment, sir. Do you want them in *before* the coffin, or following on?'

Fortunately I had thought about this aspect of the service beforehand, and I was ready with my reply.

'I'd like to suggest that they are seated first of all, and then I'll lead the coffin in. In fact, if I go and put my cotta and stole on now, we can start as soon as you like.'

I quickly reflected that I was beginning to sound as if I knew what I was doing.

Back in the sacristy I had just begun to put on my

cotta, when two of the men from the funeral directors came in.

'Sorry, sir, but I think you've got the only toilet,' said the first of them gruffly. 'Do you mind, sir?'

'Be my guest,' I ventured in a jolly voice.

The man went into the toilet and shut the door behind him, only to emerge some four or five seconds later to say that the electric light had gone off. His mate, who was half as tall again as the first man but only a third as wide, discovered that the light worked if you held the light bulb firmly in place. Thus it was that, as I was attempting to collect my thoughts, a very fat man was relieving himself energetically into the adjacent toilet, while a worryingly thin man, with the help of a leather glove, was holding in place an increasingly hot light bulb. I began to feel as if complete hysteria might be just around the corner.

I hastily positioned myself at the main door of the chapel and the mourners began to file in, led by Martha and Maria. About eight or ten people of various sizes and ages followed behind, and none of them looked at me in any way other than one which suggested complete confidence in my ability to 'get us through'. Out of the corner of my eye I could see the bearers approaching with the coffin. I swallowed hard, took a deep breath and launched myself into what seemed like an abyss of a service with the words from John's gospel that begin the Anglican rite:

Jesus said, I am the resurrection, and I am the life; he who believes in me, though he die, yet shall he live, and whoever lives and believes in me shall never die.

As the words left my lips, I felt a huge weight being lifted from my shoulders.

* * *

The service went off well, and Martha seemed genuinely moved and pleased by what I had to say about her father — even though I had, of course, only been able to play back to her the things which she had told me about him.

At the graveside I had worn Stephen's cloak to keep off the drizzle which was falling. Importantly I had managed not to slip on the damp boards around the grave. By all accounts the whole thing had passed off more successfully than I could have dared to hope, and by the time I returned to the car for the drive home I was feeling drained but happy.

I already knew that any recollections of this day could only ever bring a smile to my face. And although I had never known him, I couldn't help thinking that that was just what Nobby would have wanted.

SEVEN

Lent appeal

*So we are ambassadors for Christ, since God
is making his appeal through us.*
(2 Corinthians 5:20)

IT WAS decided that Shrove Tuesday would be a good
occasion for a party. Canon George had been talking
for some time about arranging a 'bit of a do' for
church newcomers, and it was agreed by everyone
that Shrove Tuesday would be ideal. Thus it was that
letters had gone out from the vicar and from
Stephen to all those people who were 'new' to the
parish – or at least new to the Sunday morning congregations at both St Mary's and St John's. The party
would be at the vicarage and begin at eight p.m.

I arrived at eight on the dot. The door swung
open in answer to my push of the bell, and I was
confronted by about twelve rubicund faces all
smiling hideously in my direction.

'Oh, it's only Michael,' said Kay, the vicar's wife,
with an air of disappointment. The hideous smiles
disappeared, to be replaced by more normal expressions of greeting. I walked into the hallway, nodding
knowingly at the assembled group of church
worthies, and recognizing at once that there was not
a 'newcomer' in sight.

Kay drifted back towards me, her lips pursed
together in deep understanding.

'Well, it *is* only *just* eight o'clock,' she said, as if
the situation needed some explanation. 'If you're

new, you don't want to be one of the first, do you?'

I said of course not, and allowed myself to be guided through to where Canon George was manning the drinks table.

'So what's it to be, Michael? Red or white?'

'Orange, please,' I said unenthusiastically, and felt called upon to add 'I'm driving'. I slurped noisily at my wine glass of juice, and wandered back into the wide hallway where the oldcomers were gathered, waiting for their prey.

Poor things, I thought to myself. Any minute now some poor unsuspecting newcomers are going to be the first to arrive, to be greeted by the massed ranks of the Finance and General Support Committee (FAGS for short) bearing down on them with glasses of Liebfraumilch and saucers of cheese nibbles. It's just not a fair contest, I reflected.

I gripped the banister to steady myself as the doorbell rang. Quickly everyone shifted into position, forming a wide horseshoe around the edge of the carpet. Hideous smiles were adopted all round, but were, again, destined to disappointment.

'Oh, it's only Malcolm,' they all sighed, as the organist shuffled past in trainers and anorak.

'Well, I know I've at least *one* newcomer coming,' announced Stephen confidently, as if his contribution to the evening's proceedings was in doubt. The faces of the assembled crew brightened noticeably at this news.

'Yes,' he continued. 'Mrs Moss has assured me that she will be here.'

A few of the faces dropped. Others adopted that 'well, beggars can't be choosers' expression. Alan Watts was more outspoken.

'She's not a newcomer,' he said. 'She's been going

to St John's for at least a year.'

'Well, perhaps not *new*,' said Stephen, slightly defensively. 'But newish. That is, she says she's never been to a newcomer's party.'

A stentarian voice cut across the room.

'I've never been to a newcomer's party either – and I've been coming for twenty years,' said John Burgess, staring threateningly at everyone in that slightly manic way of his. John and his wife Rose were known to Stephen and myself as 'the prophets', largely because of their regular and severe pronouncements on the state of the church today.

An embarrassed silence descended on the company, and people suddenly found their shoes to be of great interest. Joy Bartholomew attempted to come to the rescue.

'We are all newcomers in God's eyes,' she said, her eyes rolling ominously in her pinched and intent face.

There was no answer to that, and the assembled company broke up again into ones and twos to continue their interrupted murmurings. It was only a few minutes later, however, when the first new face arrived.

The door swung open to reveal a surprisingly normal-looking woman of about thirty-five. She looked genuinely surprised to see so many faces grinning at her, and appeared to take one step back. At this movement, Alan Watts leaped forward and grasped her by the elbow.

'Ahhh,' he crooned beguilingly. 'It's Mrs . . . that is Miss . . . I mean, it's very good to see you. Come. Let us give you something to drink. Something to nibble even.'

I caught the eye of Stephen who seemed to be of

the same mind on the subject of Alan's choice of words. The woman at the door became increasingly panic-stricken. She tried to speak.

'But I . . . I . . . I'm the Betterware lady. I've just come for the catalogue back!'

'Of course you are,' came Kay's voice soothingly above the hubbub, as the vicar's wife made her way through the assembled crowd to the front door.

'That's it. Put the Betterware lady down, Alan. There's a good fellow.'

Alan let go of the woman's elbow, while Kay presented her with a catalogue in a plastic bag. Much relieved, the Betterware lady clutched the catalogue to her bosom and escaped back into the night without another word. An air of desperation began to grip the would-be ambassadors for Christ.

'Are we never to get a newcomer?' cried Mary

West plaintively. But at that moment the door opened yet again, this time to reveal the presence of someone who had most certainly been invited as a 'newcomer'.

'Good evening, Mrs Moss,' chimed Stephen. 'Come and join the happy throng.'

* * *

By half past eight there were fourteen bona fide newcomers in the vicarage, and Canon George was looking pretty smug. They had arrived in groups of four or five — which was probably a matter of coincidence, but appeared to suggest a policy of safety in numbers.

I was in the corner with the rubber plant, trying to fend off a woman who looked as if she might have been a wrestler before she became a Christian.

'So you're not the vicar,' she said, clearly disappointed and confused by my dog collar and yellow clerical shirt.

'No. I'm the deacon,' I said, knowing once again that this was not an answer likely to prove conclusive.

'Does that mean you're *going* to be a vicar?'.

'No, it doesn't. I'm an NSM. That is, a Non-Stipendiary Minister. It means I don't get paid for doing this. You see, I've got a *proper* job as well.'

I said this with what I thought was the twinkle of a smile. It was supposed to be something of a joke. The woman (whose name I discovered was Mrs Clubb) stared at me stonily and nodded, so I carried on.

'Some people call it being a Minister in Secular Employment. An MSE. You see?'

She stared at me gravely.

'There are a lot of letters involved, aren't there?' she said.

'I'm sorry?' I craned forward, trying to avoid the rubber plant.

'A lot of letters,' she repeated. 'MSN, ME. . . What you said just now. My daughter's an SRN. Or, that is, she *was*. She's called something different now.'

I nodded sagely and looked over Mrs Clubb's shoulder, but the escape route was cut off.

'So who's the curate then?' Mrs Clubb was not to be put off.

'Well, I am. Sort of. And so is Stephen. Sort of.'

'But I thought you said you were the deacon. And I thought Stephen was the priest at St John's,' she persisted.

'Well, he is. Sort of,' I said, feeling my imagination running low.

'There seems to be a lot of "sort of" about it,' said Mrs Clubb.

'About it?'

'About the church. A lot of "sort of". Why can't it be one thing or another, that's what I want to know. Last week I asked Stephen if he really believed in angels, and he said he "sort of" believed in them. What sort of an answer is that, I ask you? There are either angels or there aren't, it seems to me. And there are either vicars, or there aren't. What's all this "sort of" got to do with it, that's what I want to know?'

I made a comment to the effect that Mrs Clubb had probably touched upon one of the great mysteries that had engaged the human mind since the beginning of time. She looked pleased at that, and so I felt that I could now disengage without appearing to be rude. With a last conspiratorial wink – meant to convey to Mrs Clubb my feeling that she was close to solving the question behind the whole of human existence – I edged away slowly.

As I turned towards the kitchen door, however, I was halted in my tracks by a growling sound which appeared to come from a point about two feet below my line of vision. I looked down to see Rose Burgess, grimacing up at me from a low stool.

'I blame Cranmer,' she growled, showing off her large teeth to good effect.

'Indeed,' I responded with a look of approbation, before slipping past her and into the kitchen.

Around the central table stood three people, each of whom was picking in some way at the provisions laid out there. One of the three was Kay who was looking wanly back at a man called Derek as he drew patterns in the cheese dip to illustrate something about the greenhouse effect. The third person was a slightly-built woman in her twenties. As I later found out, her mother was Taiwanese, and delicate oriental characteristics were clear, though muted, in the daughter's features.

'Hello, I'm Michael,' I said breezily, before stuffing my mouth full of cheese and chive crisps.

The young woman introduced herself as Josie, a nurse recently based at the local hospital. I could see, out of the corner of my eye, that Kay appeared about to implicate me in Derek's bleak analysis of the approaching apocalypse, and so I steered Josie away from the table and into a relatively quiet corner.

'So what made you decide to come to St Mary's?' I said, feeling that I had seen her a few times in the congregation on Sunday mornings.

'It's the closest,' she replied. 'I live in the block of flats over the road, so it would seem silly to go anywhere else.'

I smiled at the simplicity of her answer. Somehow I had got used to people haranguing me about why they had chosen one church over another because they didn't like the vicar at one, or because it was either too high or too low, or because of the music, and so on. I reflected that so often nowadays congregations in urban churches are made up largely by people who live outside the parish.

'And so what do you make of all this?' I continued. 'I mean, this newcomers' party. Do you think it's a good idea? Because I have to admit that it's the first one I've been to, and I'm interested to know if it's hitting the right note.'

'I think it's fine,' said Josie in a tone that conveyed neither enthusiasm nor criticism. She then smiled broadly as she continued. 'It's given me a chance to see inside the vicarage.'

I smiled back, noticing over Josie's shoulder that Derek was being graphic with a stick of celery and a water biscuit.

'I'm not sure it's really my thing, though,' Josie went on.

'Not your thing?' I looked back at her large brown eyes.

'Church community, or whatever you choose to call it.'

My expression must have invited more explanation.

'Well, to give you an example,' she continued. 'Soon after I arrived somebody — a very nice and warm man, certainly — started talking to me about whether or not I had thought about direct debit as a way of giving to the church. And then a very charming lady asked if I had ever considered helping at Sunday School.'

She blinked up at me as if to say 'need I go on?'

I coughed. 'Hm. Yes. I see what you mean,' I

ventured, before adding, by way of mitigation, 'They're all terribly keen to build up the church. That is, what it *is*, and what it *does*. In many respects, you represent a great potential resource for them.'

'Quite,' she said, again with disarming directness. 'And I'm not saying that's wrong. But it's not what I come to church for. I work hard all week at something I enjoy enormously, but also at something that takes a great deal out of me. Physically and emotionally. When I come to church on a Sunday morning it is, if you'll forgive the expression, to have my batteries recharged. It gives me a space and a time in which I can relax. I can feel my spirit growing in that space and that time, and I go out again refreshed and ready for another week at the hospital. You see, ultimately I don't think that my relationship with God is about money, or Sunday School, or many of the things that go on in and around the church as such.'

She looked at me apologetically, as if she were somehow speaking out of turn. I asked her to go on.

'You must think I'm here under false pretences,' she said. 'I don't think I am. I *do* actually want to know the people who make up the community at St Mary's. But I'm already clear in my own mind that my relationship with God is mainly worked out in my time at the hospital, and that when I come to church it is to be refreshed and nourished for that work. To be quite honest, if the Sunday morning services took place in a wooden hut, I would be just as happy. I'm sorry. That's not really the right thing to say to a vicar, is it?'

- I stopped myself from making any comment about vicars, curates and deacons, and exhaled deeply. I wanted to tell Josie that what she had said was the most interesting thing I had heard all evening, but I was worried that it might sound patronizing or glib.

'I think that so often we undervalue the lives we live as Christians in the wider world.' In most cases this might have been my introduction to a brief excursion on my role as a minister with 'a proper job', but somehow it did not seem the right time.

'And I'm glad,' I added, 'that you can feel refreshed and nourished at St Mary's.'

At this point I felt I could not resist the temptation to plug the Ash Wednesday service which would be on the following evening.

'Are you coming to our Ash Wednesday Eucharist tomorrow night?' I asked. '*Despite* the fact that I'm preaching,' I said with a smile, 'you may nevertheless find *something* there to refresh you!'

Josie smiled back a confident smile of maturity, understanding and true Christian love.

'Church twice in one week! Now that really *would* be a luxury,' she said, adding impishly, 'I think I'll just worship while I'm on the ward.'

For once no trite comment sprang to my lips. It was, I reflected, at times like this that my collar seemed to chafe most.

* * *

I decided to walk to St Mary's for the Ash Wednesday evening service, and as I made my way past the neat rows of nineteen-thirties semis, I tried to recall what Canon George had told me by way of preparation.

The service would follow the usual pattern for a Eucharist, but would for the first time at St Mary's include the 'Imposition of Ashes'. This was a tradition that had been in place at St John's for a number of years, but had not until now been part of the church year at St Mary's. It involved using ash at one particular point in the service to produce the mark of a cross on the forehead of each worshipper as a sign of penitence.

I had first attended a service of this kind at St John's a few years before, and remembered acutely how self-conscious I had felt on leaving the church with what I could only imagine was a big black smudge across my forehead. Whilst being generally in favour of the use of symbolism in worship, there was nevertheless a bit of me that felt it was slightly absurd to daub the heads of hard-core parishioners with a prominent dirty mark.

Canon George was, however, determined to widen the range of services in the parish, and he had fixed on Lent and Easter as a time when he could include some innovations at St Mary's that would, he hoped, accommodate both the Catholic and the Evangelical interests in the congregation.

We had run through the changes in the liturgy a few days before and, as I walked along on that Ash Wednesday evening, I tried to remember what it was that I was supposed to say as the black mark was placed upon the virgin scalp. For Canon George had told me that he would like me to share in the Imposition of Ashes.

'Remember that you are dust, and to dust you shall return.' I managed to say it in time to the rhythm of my steps as I walked along.

'Remember that you are dust, and to dust you shall return.' One, two, three, four.

'Remember that you are dust, and to dust you shall return.' Over and over again, until I felt that it was ingrained in my very soul. There would be no excuse now if I forgot what to say.

When I arrived at St Mary's I went straight to the vestry, where Canon George was preparing the ashes for the service. At this stage the ashes were in the form of a pile of sooty black powder in an old tobacco tin. Canon George had collected together a number of palm crosses that parishioners had kept from the previous Palm Sunday. He had then burned them in the bowl of his small barbecue to produce the black ashes. These rather dusty remnants were, however, not ideal for marking foreheads, and so they had to be mixed into a sort of damp paste.

Canon George decanted the powder into a small, shallow bowl, and then added a few drops of holy oil, before blending the whole lot with the help of an apostle teaspoon. The resultant black gritty paste was, he assured me, just the right consistency for making crosses on people's heads.

I looked admiringly down at the messy mixture. Who was I to say anything different? I could probably have travelled the Christian world and not found a better mix of soot and oil. I nodded sagely, and then said solemnly:

'I think I've got the words off.'

'Got the words off *what*?' said Canon George.

'No. I mean, I've learned the words.'

Canon George looked at me blankly.

'Remember that you are dust, and to dust you shall return,' I said triumphantly.

'Oh, *those* words,' said the Canon. He paused momentarily and looked at me, before saying:

'Well, go on then. What about the next bit?'

Next bit? What next bit? I looked back at him, puzzled. He put down his bowl of ash and smiled one of his most disconcertingly supportive smiles.

'"Remember that you are dust, and to dust you shall return. Turn away from sin, and be faithful to Christ." Two lines, you see. It's probably best if you make the mark on the forehead with your thumb as you say the first line — downward stroke, and then sideways stroke — and then, if it hasn't come out very well, you've got the chance to do it once more while you say the second line. When you think about it, it's quite sensible really.'

Quite sensible! My mind was racing.

'Good Lord,' I said without thinking. 'You mean there's a second line? What happens if I forget it?'

'Forget it? Oh, no. You won't forget it,' said Canon George. 'And if you do . . . Well, that is . . . Oh, don't worry. You won't forget it!'

I thought to myself that I could write it down on a card and keep it in my pocket. But that wouldn't be any use, I remembered, because I would have soot and oil all over my right hand, and be holding a dish of ash mix in my left. There was nothing for it. I would have to trust my memory. After all, I had a full ten minutes to get the words ingrained into my soul alongside the others.

As I put on my vestments, I paced up and down in the vestry reciting the lines to myself.

'Remember you are dust, and to dust you shall return. Be faithful to . . .' No, that's not right.

'Turn to Christ, and be faithful.' No, wrong again.

'Turn away from sin.' Is *that* it?

'Canon George,' I asked at last. '*What* did you say that line was again?'

'Turn away from sin and be faithful to Christ,' he said, looking up from his dish with an ash-smudged nose.

'Right,' I said grimly. 'Got it.'

* * *

The service progressed as a fairly normal Eucharist. I read the gospel (the bit about how we mustn't look gloomy when we fast), and then I preached a sermon. I was determined not to bang on only about penitence and sacrifice and all that stuff, but I also judged that the time was probably not right for some of my jokes. So I preached a fairly straight little number that tried to strike a positive note about the *appeal* of Lent. Something to be looked forward to.

As I gripped the edges of the lectern and gazed around at the scattered faces in the pews, I could not find one person whose expression conveyed anything that bore out my assumed optimism about the season that was upon us.

'Remember!' I exhorted the congregation, suddenly seeing in my mind's eye the words of a poster that I had bought in Carnaby Street in 1967. 'Tomorrow is the first day of the rest of your life!'

It was supposed to be a cry of hope and optimism, but the words seemed to be met by my hearers with looks of resignation, despair, and even horror. One wizened old woman, whom I had seen on only one or two occasions before, fixed me with a particularly threatening look as she screwed up her hymn sheet into a small ball. How dare I (the look seemed to say) sound so terribly bland and optimistic! This was Lent, for God's sake! I had no business being cheerful.

I made my final pronouncements in a sombre tone, and walked wearily back to my seat in the sanctuary, ready for the penitential section of the service. We said the words of the general confession, and then Canon George and I went behind the altar — my mind racing once again to try to remember the words.

We faced each other and Canon George picked up one of two dishes of ash. He planted his thumb in the mixture, and then made the sign of the cross on my forehead as he said:

'Remember that you are dust, and to dust you shall return. Turn away from sin and be faithful to Christ.'

I then took the dish from him and, with quivering thumb, made a cross-like mark on his head that went from his hairline right down to the bridge of his nose, and was about two inches across.

As I stood back and looked at it, I thought 'That's a bit big, really', and the tidy side of my nature wanted to reach out and rub part of it off again. Never mind, I thought, at least I remembered the words.

By now the other members of the sanctuary party (the crucifier, servers and acolytes) had lined up in front of the altar. Canon George made his way to the right-hand end of the line, and I moved menacingly towards the left-hand end, carrying my little dish of ash.

The first person I came to was Maurice, the piratical crucifier. I leaned reverently over him, and pushed my sooty thumb towards his face, suddenly conscious that I would have to try to avoid the elastic of his eye-patch. Unfortunately, this was enough to throw me off course.

'Remember that you are dust, and to dust you shall return. Turn away from Christ . . .' I stopped what I was saying, but carried on making the sign of the cross. Unable to think what exactly I had said wrong, I simply added 'and be faithful', before standing back to look at my handiwork.

Maurice and his one eye were gazing back at me

with a look of spectacular bewilderment.

'Turn away from Christ?' he muttered, almost to himself.

I then realized what I had said, but wasn't sure whether there was time for me to 'do' him again. To do that might draw attention to my gaffe, and it was just possible that Maurice might have objected to having his forehead used in such a free and easy manner. I decided to press on.

After the sanctuary party had been ashed, Canon George and I stood ready while the members of the congregation came forward. He and I took half the communion rail each, and I began to mark the assembled foreheads with a sense of energetic purpose, never once forgetting again the correct form of words.

When it was done, Canon George and I returned our used dishes of ash paste to the altar and then realized that we had made no provision for cleaning our fingers and thumbs. We both dug around inside our robes for handkerchiefs so that we could then make some attempt to wipe off the remains of the sooty residue before continuing.

From then on the service progressed much as usual. As I stood behind the altar, however, looking out at the serried rows of parishioners, I kept asking myself what it was all about. What would each of them take away from the service? Other than a black smudge, of course. Would the more Catholic-minded people feel encouraged by this style of service? Would the more Evangelical feel awkward or offended? To whom were we supposed to be appealing? Newcomers or oldcomers? And how would we ever know if we were getting it right?

* * *

At the end of the service, Canon George and I positioned ourselves either side of the main door, smiling in a sympathetic and Lent-like way as members of the congregation moved slowly towards us in ones and twos. Some of them may have seen Canon George and I passing comments to each other, and it may have been assumed that we were swapping news about matters liturgical or pastoral.

As it was, we were comparing notes on the quality of the ash crosses that we had each been dispensing earlier. Comments such as:

'That's a good one on Geoffrey Newton's head. Was that you or me?'

'I don't think much of the one you gave Lynda Soames.'

'Only two out of ten for Barbara Bailey's. It's not in the middle, and I can't see the downward bit at all.'

'That's a cracker on Frank Foster. Mind you, you did have a lot of forehead to play with.'

'Good Lord! Did you do Penny Wainwright with your eyes shut?'

And so it was that our flock made their way out into the crisp night air. On their heads at least they carried the signs of soot and oil. Perhaps in their hearts they also carried the marks of penitence and sacrifice.

Certainly as I made my own way home later that night, I reflected that there had to be a God — and a loving God at that — to have created his ambassadors in such a frail, absurd and dependent mould.

EIGHT

Pick 'n' mix

*Again, truly I tell you, if two of you agree on
earth about anything you ask, it will be
done for you by my Father in heaven.*
(Matthew 18:19)

APART from the ashing on Ash Wednesday, Canon
George had suggested a few other innovations for
the period of Lent. One of them concerned study
groups. As well as the usual sequence of Lent study
groups that met in people's houses, he had put
together a programme of five special meetings to
take place in St Mary's Church Hall. Each one was
to be led by a member of the parish with the objective of trying to draw together his or her direct
experience of life with different elements from the
Gospel.

The first one had featured Lucy Floyd, a regular
worshipper at St John's and one of the new breed of
health service managers at the local hospital. She
had led an evening discussion on 'Healing — the
best practice', during which she drew a rather
dubious parallel between Jesus's commissioning of
the disciples and the setting up of hospital trusts.

The second session had been led by Alan Watts on
the subject of 'Service — the denial of self'. Alan
was a retired member of the Civil Service, and I felt
this was a somewhat tenuous link. As it turned out,
'service' featured only in passing during a long
three-hour session in which we were shown Alan's

holiday slides from his visit to the Holy Land the year before.

The third discussion leader in the series was to be me. The subject that Canon George and I had settled on was 'Creation — getting under the skin of the Gospel.' It was not to be about creation stories in the Bible, but rather on creative ways to approach an understanding of the Gospel. It was supposed to give me an opportunity to use one or two of the techniques which were employed in brainstorming sessions at the advertising agency.

When the idea had first been put to me I had welcomed it as a chance to introduce something a bit different to a number of the parishioners whom I only encountered on Sunday mornings. The first two sessions in the series had, however, taken their toll. The enthusiasm of many of the occasional churchgoers had noticeably waned.

Lucy's evening meeting had attracted about fifty people, a very good turnout by normal parish standards. Alan's excursion into holiday snaps had played to about thirty. By the time my own slot on creativity arrived, the number had dropped to about twenty — most of whom were those stalwarts of the parish who would have turned up to listen to the Rural Dean read aloud from the Thirty-Nine Articles.

Such devotion from the few would at least, I reflected, ensure a respectable attendance for the remaining two sessions. The very next one was to be Malcolm Potts on 'Music — what does the Gospel teach us?'. I remember that when this had been discussed at the last clergy staff meeting, Stephen had said 'Music? In the Gospel? *What* music?', only to be told by Canon George that God moved in mysterious ways and that we should all have to 'wait and see'.

This beacon of scriptural revelation was, however, still only a glimmer in the future as I sat in the church hall on a chilly March evening waiting for people to arrive. As I sat waiting I became conscious of a slight soreness of the throat. Nerves, I thought. I'll have a boiled sweet. I had brought with me a large bag of sweets and I fished around to find a fat orange lozenge. It would take some sucking, but I knew that I still had plenty of time. The meeting was to begin in a few minutes at eight o'clock but, as usual with church meetings, most people would arrive late.

Colin was the first to poke a head warily around the edge of the door, closely followed by 'the two Mary's' — as Stephen and I called Mary Brown and Mary West, who were always together despite the fact that they seemed so unalike. Then came Hilary Noble and Alan Watts, Lynda Soames, Doreen Butcher and, of course, Frank Foster. Christine the Mystic and Penny Wainwright arrived with Joy Bartholomew in tow. Then came a string of souls, led by Canon George himself. Geoffrey Newton, Barbara Bailey and 'the prophets' — John and Rose Burgess. Finally I was very glad to see Dawn Copeland and a couple of unknown quantities sliding in at the back. Dawn, and her husband Trevor, had four children between the ages of four and ten, and so it was often difficult for them to come to evening meetings.

'Right,' I said, smiling broadly at the horseshoe of faces that stared apprehensively in my direction after the opening prayer. 'Tonight our subject is "Creation — getting under the skin of the Gospel", and I'd like to begin by asking you all to take a sweet from this bag that I'm going to pass around. At lunch time I went to the Pick 'n' Mix counter of Woolworth's near to where I work and I bought myself a selection of sweets. I'd like you all to take one — but don't eat it! Well, not yet, at least. First of all, I want you to *talk* about the sweet you have picked.'

'Michael?' came a plaintive voice from the front row.

'Yes, Joy?'

'I don't like sweets.'

'Well, you don't have to eat it, Joy. Not if you don't want to. Just talk about it.'

'But I don't like them.'

'Very well, Joy. Just pass the bag on to the next person, will you? That's it. Now, the next thing I want you to do is to think about the sweet you have in your hand. It may be a truffle. It may be a humbug or a liquorice allsort. Whatever it is, I want you to look at it carefully and imagine what its *character* would be if it had a character.'

'Michael,' said Mary Brown, fluttering her eyelashes at me in her usual coquettish way.

'Yes, Mary.'

'I can't look at my sweet. I'm afraid I've eaten it already.'

'Now, I did ask you not to eat it just yet, didn't I? Never mind.'

'She can have mine,' said Joy helpfully. 'She can have the one I didn't have. You can have mine, Mary.'

'Yes, thank you, Joy,' I said through a forced smile.

It was at this point that I became aware that my sore throat was a sign that I should have stayed at home and watched something terribly boring on the television. I gritted my teeth, however, and informed the group that there were more sweets in the bag than there were people in the room, and that Mary could have her pick of what remained.

'So,' I said, trying to smile again. 'Who can tell me about the character of their sweet?'

'A sweet doesn't have a character,' said Doreen in that determined way that seemed to challenge any further conversation on the point.

'Oh, but it does,' crooned Geoffrey. He looked in my direction for support and I waved a hand vaguely in the air as a sign that he should go on. Geoffrey Newton was a thirty-five-year-old man with a beard and lots of corduroys. He and his wife Amanda both worked for charities and, with no children to look after, spent much of their spare time singing in various choirs. They were both great liberals in every aspect of life, and church was no exception. It was therefore a matter of principle that Geoffrey should take issue with Doreen over anything.

'I've never been able to eat humbugs,' continued Geoffrey. 'They always seem so pompous and old-fashioned. My own sweet this evening is a truffle. Soft and interesting, delicately wrapped in red foil.'

'Thank you, Geoffrey,' I said, deciding that this was the moment to help things along. 'Now, Geoffrey has given us a very good example of character in a sweet. So what is your sweet, then, Doreen?'

I felt that by inviting her to respond I could begin to repair any damage done.

'A humbug,' she said fiercely, fixing first Geoffrey and then me with a withering stare.

'If I may,' ventured Canon George, always the reconciler. 'I feel that sweets, and their characters, are very much what we make of them. Let me give you an example. I have picked a liquorice allsort. Now I love liquorice allsorts because they always remind me of Christmas, for some reason or other. But I know that my wife Kay hates them because they remind her of her Uncle Fergus.'

I wasn't sure that this intervention by the vicar had necessarily moved the discussion on, but at least everyone was now nodding sagely. The canon had, as far as everyone could ascertain, 'put his finger on it'.

'Right,' I said once more, steeling myself for yet another rebuff. 'Are there any more sweet characters that people would like to mention before we move on and eat them?'

Dawn Copeland quietly said that she had a pink shrimp which she thought was weak and vulnerable. Alan had an aniseed ball that 'knew where it was going in life'. Penny Wainwright had a jelly baby whom she thought was supercilious and needed its head bitten off.

These were the kind of comments that I had been hoping for. Some of the other comments, however, were more, let us say, tangential.

First Joy had re-entered the discussion with a comment to the effect that there hadn't been many home-made biscuits at the last 'bring and buy sale'. I manoeuvred the topic back towards the sweets, only to run straight into an enthusiastic Rose Burgess.

'My sweet is a toffee,' she crowed in a high-pitched and earnest tone. 'It's character is that it gets stuck to my dentures.'

'That's very good,' joined in John Burgess, sounding slightly less prophetic than usual, and smiling admiringly at his wife's imaginative powers. 'They do indeed get stuck to her plate!'

'Right,' I replied. 'Well, thank you for sharing that with us, Rose.'

It was then that Frank chimed in, obviously feeling that it was now open season for wit and ribaldry.

'I've got a clear mint. As mints go, I always think these are a bit insincere. Well, let's put it this way. I can always see through them.'

Everyone groaned and looked at the ceiling whilst Frank grinned horribly at the assembled company.

'Yes, well, thank you, Frank,' I said. 'Can I suggest that we all now eat our sweets? Good. Right. Well, I expect you're all wondering why I asked you to do that?'

I could see a few movements which did nothing to put me at my ease. Doreen crossed her arms. Colin put his head on one side. Mary West took out a pencil as if to write down the incriminating evidence for future reference.

'It was simply to demonstrate that a little bit of imagination can start to bring to life the most inanimate of objects. Like a sweet. Imagination is not just something that so-called imaginative people use. It's something we *all* use when we start filling in the gaps. The gaps between one known thing and another. That's largely how we use imagination in advertising. First of all we get to know as much as we can about a *product*. Then we get to know as much as we can about the *people* who are likely to want to buy it. And then we use our imaginations to find ways in which the gap between product and person can be filled. Does that make any sense?'

There were a lot of blank looks around. I decided to press on.

'Let me try to give you an example. One of the products I'm developing advertising for at the moment is a pizza. Now, if I were trying to advertise pizzas specifically to a churchgoing group of people like you, then I would use my imagination to fill the gap between your particular interests and the pizzas.'

I paused and thought about my sore throat. The delay was fatal. Barbara Bailey filled the vacuum with words that immediately gave me a sinking feeling.

'Go on then, Michael,' she said imperiously. 'Tell us how you might do it.'

'Yes,' added Christine the Mystic. 'Be creative in front of our very eyes.'

I squirmed in my seat as Christine leaned forward and began to take an unnatural interest in me.

'Well,' I said slowly, playing for time. 'I might come up with an advertising idea to do with religion. Like an angel, or a spirit, or a god, or something else like that. A religious way of selling pizzas, if you see what I mean.'

And then an idea struck me.

'How about this?' I said, feeling that I had managed to dig myself out of a hole. 'Deep peace from the deep pan — Pronto Pizzas are a real blessing.'

There were one or two low-key smiles, but again a lot of blank looks. I tried again.

'Deep peace from the deep pan,' I said again. 'A real blessing. Or perhaps a Godsend.'

'Oh, I see,' said Frank at last. 'Very droll.'

'Droll?' said Doreen in a low and threatening

tone. 'Only if you think it's droll to speak of God and pizzas in the same breath.'

'I think God can be spoken of in the same breath as *anything*,' said Geoffrey, once again spurred on by Doreen. 'After all he did create everything — if you believe the traditional accounts.' This last comment was accompanied by a look that I can only refer to as a leer, and Doreen stiffened her back in response.

'I had a pizza once,' said Joy, 'but I didn't like it.'

'Just like the sweets, I suppose,' said Mary Brown, trying to be helpful. 'They don't agree with you, I suppose.'

'I don't agree with Geoffrey,' said Barbara.

'I'm sorry,' I gasped, losing track of where exactly the conversation was going.

'Geoffrey,' said Barbara. 'He said that God can be spoken of in the same breath as anything. Well, I don't agree.'

'Nor do I,' said Doreen.

'The grapes of wrath,' moaned John Burgess ominously.

'Pardon, John?' I prompted. But John was shaking his head and looking at his feet with an intensity that forbade any disturbance.

'Well, I think Geoffrey is right,' asserted Penny.

'Thank you, Penny,' said Geoffrey.

It was at this point that Canon George intervened once more.

'Ladies and gentlemen. If I may just place a thought in your heads. And that is that "where two or three are gathered in my name, I am there among them". That is all.'

As usual Canon George's calm presence brought everyone back together again. In fact, I immediately found myself caught in a crossfire of apologies and acceptances, as everyone made up and said things like 'You know I don't mean it personally' and 'When we disagree, of course, we do it in love'.

This whole episode left me rather bemused, and so when Colin asked 'where were we?', I found I had lost track entirely of what the discussion had been about. Fortunately, after a few seconds, Mary West looked up from her notes to say that I had been speaking about how imagination can fill gaps.

'Thank you, Mary,' I said relieved to be back on some kind of course. 'Yes, as I was saying, imagination can help to fill some of the gaps.' It was at this point that I reached for my Bible as a source of both reassurance and inspiration.

'It can also,' I said, 'help us to get under the skin of the Gospel. Now some of you will be familiar with projective techniques in reading the Bible and in praying — but for some it may be a new experience. What it means, basically, is that you use your imagination to enter into a biblical scene. Now, who has done that before?'

A few hands went up. The ones I would have predicted: Geoffrey, Christine, Penny. Most stayed down.

'Well, tonight I want to look at one small part of the Bible and to use our imaginations to get under the skin, as it were, of what's going on.'

'Surely it's clear already what's going on,' said Lynda. 'You only have to read it, and it's as clear as day. That's why you only ever need the Gospel. It's as clear as clear can be.'

'In its way, it is,' creaked Colin, screwing his eyes up to show deep thought and concentration. 'But it has always been illuminated by the tradition within which we read it.'

'If you read the right one,' chipped in Doreen sternly. 'I don't see why we can't still use the *proper* Bible.'

'The *proper* Bible?' asked Mary Brown, looking a picture of vagueness.

'The King James Bible,' added Barbara authoritatively.

'Which no one born in the second half of the twentieth century can understand. Which is why I use the Good News Bible for the older children in the Sunday School,' said Penny, tight-lipped.

'Well, I have to say that *all* texts are corrupt,' said Geoffrey, throwing in his own contribution to this little diversion. 'It's just a question of finding one that's less corrupt than the others.'

'Corruption, corruption!' intoned John. 'All is corruption!'

John's words had the effect of stopping everyone else, and so I had the opportunity to speak.

'Yes, well once again, thank you all for sharing those thoughts with us. But if I might come back to my original point. Which was just to say that our imaginations can be helpful when we read the Bible — whatever version we are reading, and whatever we may think about the precise role of the Bible in our own spiritual journeys.'

Phew, I thought. That was a close one. Still, we're not out of the woods yet. But let's at least get them opening their Bibles and focusing on the Word, I thought. I quickly asked everyone to turn to Mark's version of the feeding of the five thousand.

'Now, I want you to read through chapter six, verses thirty-four to forty-four. We'll sit quietly for a few minutes while we do that.'

There then followed a period of intense quiet as

they all studiously applied themselves to the text. After a few minutes, when I could see that most faces were towards me, I started speaking again.

'Does anyone have anything immediate that he or she wishes to say? Yes, Joy.'

'I don't like fish.'

'You don't like fish,' I repeated.

'I like bread, though.'

'Well, that's good, then, Joy. Perhaps if you had been there you would have just had bread.'

Fortunately Joy did not pursue the point, so I was able to continue.

'Joy has obviously already entered into the spirit of this little exercise. Her first reaction was to the *physicality* of what was on offer to the five thousand. Which is to say that her reaction was a reaction of the imagination. Now, that's what I would like us all to do. To read through the passage once again, and this time to try to enter imaginatively into what is going on in the story. And then we'll see what comes out.'

Again, the silence was broken only by the whirring of minds as we all applied ourselves to the task.

'OK,' I said at last. 'Now what we're really trying to do is use our imaginations to get under the skin of the gospel in this particular passage. So what sort of things occur to you first of all?'

'I don't like the way Jesus told everyone to sit down on the grass,' said Mary Brown with no hesitation.

'And why is that, Mary?' I asked, not sure that this was the direction I had hoped the discussion would take at this point.

'I can't help feeling it would be wet,' said Mary, her eyes twinkling in that knowing way. 'It

143

wouldn't be good for me. You know. My problem.'

She smiled at me winsomely.

'Piles,' said Frank.

'I'm sorry,' I said, beginning now to feel light-headed.

'It's no good sitting down on the wet if you've got piles,' continued Frank. Mary Brown looked aghast.

'Rheumatism,' she insisted breathily. 'I've got rheumatism.'

'I'm sorry. I wasn't suggesting you had anything else, Mary,' said Frank, looking rather pink. 'We all know about your rheumatism. I was just thinking that anyone with piles wouldn't want to sit down at all. Let alone on the wet grass.'

'It wouldn't be wet, I can assure you,' said Alan, sitting upright suddenly and looking around with an air of superior knowledge. 'Bridget and I went to the Holy Land last year, as some of you will recollect.' Several sets of eyes were cast heavenward. 'Whilst we were there we actually trod the same steps that Jesus trod. We walked on the same gently sloping hills, and grassy knolls — and I can certainly say that nowhere did we find any wet grass. Not in that heat. Dry as a bone it was. Which means, Mary, that you would be all right with your piles.'

'Rheumatism,' choked Mary, who was beginning to look upset.

'Can I suggest that we leave the subject of the grass?' I said, looking at my watch and wondering how soon I could finish without appearing to be 'bottling out', as they say.

'And move on to pastures new?' said Frank with a gleam in his eye.

'Whatever,' I said wearily. 'Would anyone else like to say something about imagination and the

144

story of the feeding of the five thousand?'

'My Bible says that there were five thousand men,' said Penny. 'What about the women? Weren't there any women there?'

'"Men" means "women" as well,' said Doreen.

'And I suppose "bread" means "Danish pastries" as well,' said Geoffrey jauntily.

'And what's that supposed to mean?' flashed back an aggrieved Doreen who felt herself to have been insulted.

'Only that you can't take the words to mean just what you want them to,' persisted Geoffrey.

'Why?' Lynda asked him. 'I thought that's what *you* did all the time? I'm only surprised that you haven't suggested that it never really happened anyway, and that it's all just a made-up story. A little moral tale.'

'Does it matter?'

I looked around quickly to see who had spoken. It was Christine.

'Does it matter?' she continued. 'Who are *we* to say? Who are *we* to say *anything* in the face of the ineffable one?'

'In the face of *what*?' asked Barbara.

'What was that word?' said Mary West, looking up once more from her scribbling. 'What was that "eff" word?'

'Who said "eff"?' said John, his voice wobbling with emotion. 'Oh, retribution!'

'Ineffable,' chuckled Frank. 'She said "ineffable"!'

'Well, I still don't know what it means,' said Mary West, returning to her note-taking with a dejected air.

'If something is ineffable it is too great, intense, or sacred to be talked of,' said Hilary, reminding everyone of her own intense presence.

'That's why I don't like fish,' said Joy in a way that managed to bring a hushed silence over the group.

'What do you mean, Joy?' asked Lynda with a serious and furrowed brow.

'Inedible. I think they're inedible.'

I looked quickly across to where Canon George was sitting, hoping that he would say something that would rescue the situation from impending chaos, but he remained sitting with a broad and benign smile on his face.

'If I might move us on,' I said, raising my voice just a little over what was now something of a hubbub. 'If I might move us on to consider the end of the passage. As it has it in my version, "And all ate and were filled". What do you think the gospel writer meant by that?'

There was a long and worried silence during which time several people cast sidelong glances at each other. Finally, Mary Brown said, 'Well, I'm no expert, of course, but I think it means that all ate and were filled.'

'Thank you, Mary,' I said nervously, seeing a few heads nodding vigorously at Mary's interpretation of the gospel. 'And what do you think the gospel writer actually *meant* by that?'

'Mark' barked Barbara.

'Michael, Barbara. Not Mark,' I said slightly testily, thinking that Barbara had mistaken me for someone else.

'Not *you*,' she barked back. 'The gospel writer. His name was St Mark. Why do you keep calling him "the gospel writer" when we all know his name was Mark?'

I didn't have a chance to reply before Geoffrey launched forth into a lecturette about how we couldn't be sure that anyone called Mark was the author of the gospel, and that nobody knew which Mark was being referred to anyway.

I could see Doreen winding up for a riposte, and so judged that I would have to make a swift intervention once more.

'Yes, well, thank you, Geoffrey,' I said with a slight tremor in my voice. I was now feeling quite hot and cold at the same time. 'I'm sure we would all agree that there is a great deal of the Bible about which we cannot be totally certain.'

As I said those words I knew that they were a mistake in this company, and I saw out of the corner of my eye that Lynda was about to put me right as to the absolute verity of Holy Scripture. Sensing this, I chose to plough on.

'That is,' I said, the tremor in my voice now becoming quite distinct. 'What I mean to say is that we all have different views on the matter and, indeed, on all sorts of other matters. And it ill behoves us to set up our own view as being the only one.'

I stopped suddenly and stared into space. Where on earth had that come from? That phrase — 'it ill behoves'. Not only did I not use language like that, I wasn't sure I even knew what it meant. It seemed to have crept into my speech from somewhere else, and as soon as I heard those unfamiliar words I knew that I was lost. My body felt remote and as if it had been wrapped in cotton wool. My head began to spin with a feeling of intoxication, although I knew that I had not touched a drop of drink.

Canon George must have noticed my symptoms

because it was at this point that he made his presence known.

'I think that Michael is quite right. We are all different. That is one of the beauties of creation. Each of us is quite unique and unrepeatable. And as such we all are bound to have different ways of seeing things. That is not a problem. It is a blessing. Because ultimately what is important is not the views we have as individuals, but the fact that God has chosen each one of us. He has picked us with all our differences, all our failings, all our various attempts to express what we understand of the way that God is working in the world. And having chosen us as his children, God has put us together and mixed us up.'

'And some are more mixed up than others,' Doreen said to Barbara in a loud stage whisper.

That comment was about the last one that I heard that evening. I must have looked quite unwell by that stage because Christine and Lynda came towards me and put their hands on my forehead one after the other.

'He's very hot,' said Christine.

'I think he's feverish,' added Lynda.

And with those words I was briskly, but caringly, ushered into my coat, out of the hall, into a car, and driven home. A home where I spent the next two days in bed with what I can only describe as some kind of flu.

* * *

About a week later Canon George told me that the meeting had carried on for another hour after I had left, at the end of which there had been several comments from people to the effect that 'we should have noticed from the way he was talking that he wasn't well'.

I decided to be philosophical about the whole event, and put it down to experience. I did laugh, however, when Canon George told me about Joy's diagnosis of my illness.

'It must have been the inedible fish that didn't agree with him.'

Just my luck, I thought. Not only don't the parishioners agree with me. The fish don't either.

NINE

T.G.I.F.

And what I say to you I say to all:
Keep awake. (Mark 13:37)

A BOUT of flu was not the only ill of my Lent that year. The orange juices that I drank at the newcomers' party on Shrove Tuesday had set an ominous precedent. I had returned from the Ash Wednesday service at about half past nine in the evening to find Cheryl depressed and aggressive, having given up alcohol and chocolate for one whole day. Her irritability was focused on me, whom she accused of not having the will power or discipline to give up anything for Lent. Unfortunately I was silly enough to rise to the bait.

'I can give up anything if I want to,' I said rashly.

'OK,' she said, quick as a flash. 'Give up drink. Like me. Go on. You were bragging about how you managed to get through the newcomers' party without a drop of the stuff. So give up drink for Lent.'

This was said as I was taking the bottle of gin from the cupboard, and was therefore a remark full of cruelty and spite.

'Hah!' Cheryl almost spat. 'Just as I thought. No will power. None.'

'It's nothing to do with will power,' I said patiently. 'You've given up drink because you're on some kind of fitness drive. It's nothing to do with a Lenten discipline. Well, personally, I don't want to be any fitter than I am now. I'm as fit as I need to be for what I do. There is absolutely no reason why I should want to give up drink.'

'Because you *can't* give it up!' came the reply.

Well, I won't bore you with the tedious details of the remainder of this conversation. Needless to say Cheryl won. When I could have just shrugged and sat down with a large gin and tonic, I was mad fool enough to see it as a matter of honour. To cut a long story short, by the time Holy Week arrived some six weeks later I was very dry and fairly desperate for a drink. By then, however, I knew that the moment of rescue was only a few days away, and so I approached Easter with an even greater sense of anticipation than usual.

Yes, I know that I could have drunk on Sundays and other feast days, and still claimed to have been abstemious for Lent. But that would not have been a pattern of behaviour in keeping with the principle at stake — which was all about will power. Cheryl was not eating chocolate or biscuits during Lent, neither was she drinking alcohol. I, for my part, gave up the booze with a bad grace, and made a point of conspicuously pigging out on chocolate biscuits for seven weeks.

The first couple of days of Holy Week went fairly quietly, both at work and in the parish. On Wednesday evening I went straight from the station to St John's to meet Canon George and Stephen in order to talk through how we were going to handle the Liturgy of the Cross on Good Friday afternoon. St John's had a more Catholic tradition than did St Mary's, and for this Good Friday service Canon George had planned a further addition to that tradition.

When I arrived they were standing chatting in the vestry.

'Ah, Michael,' beamed Canon George, as I put down my briefcase. 'Prostration. Stephen and I have just been discussing prostration. And how, by the way, are *you*?'

I told him I was well, and tried to catch Stephen's eye for some hint of what Canon George was talking about. Before Stephen had a chance to respond, however, Canon George was shepherding us out of the vestry and into the sanctuary, directly in front of the altar.

'We'll enter in single file,' he said. 'Then we'll turn to face the altar and prostrate ourselves. As a sign of humility. Like this.'

And without further ado, the rotund figure of Canon George fell forward onto the carpet so that he was lying stretched out and face down a few feet away from the altar.

Stephen and I looked at each other, and then at the prostrate man on the floor.

'Are you all right, George?' said Stephen.

'Perfectly,' said Canon George. 'Now, will you help me up, please?'

Stephen and I bent down and pulled the red-faced and puffing canon to his feet.

'Are you *sure* you're all right?' I said. 'I've never seen you move so fast. Did you mean to go down that quickly, or did your legs give way?'

'The trick is,' said Canon George, ignoring the smiles and winks that his two curates were exchanging, 'to fall swiftly to the knees, and then immediately forward. Trying to make the whole thing look like one movement. Now let's try it together, shall we? And let's see if we can synchronize our actions as much as possible.'

So it was that, at seven o'clock on the evening of

Wednesday in Holy Week, I was standing in one of my best suits ready to prostrate myself in a synchronized way with two men dressed in black cassocks. For some reason the term 'practising Christian' came into my mind. Sometimes I have been asked by people who don't know me (particularly, it seems, people who arrive unsolicited on my doorstep) if I am a 'practising Christian'. I've never been sure what it was exactly that I was supposed to be practising. But I suddenly became aware that, whatever else it might include, it almost certainly ought to cover the art of synchronized prostration.

'When we're on the floor,' said Canon George, 'we'll work out how long we should stay down. OK?'

'OK by me,' I said.

'Bob's your uncle,' replied Stephen with a straight face.

With that, we lined up and, at the first attempt, fell to the floor as one man. As the three of us lay there, Canon George was the first to speak.

'Bravo!' he said, as he turned his head first to me on one side of him, and then to Stephen on the other side.

Bravo indeed, I thought. Here I am, in business suit, shirt and tie, lying face down on a carpet, and my vicar said 'bravo'.

'I think we'll stay here for five seconds,' continued Canon George. 'And then, if you follow my lead, we'll get up together. One, two, three, go.'

The getting up was nothing like as smooth as the falling down, and it was accompanied by much heaving and wheezing as the three of us hauled ourselves back into fairly upright positions. By the time Canon George was vertical again, his face was the colour of beetroot, and he was breathing heavily.

'There!' he said. 'That wasn't too bad, was it?'

'Wonderful,' purred Stephen impishly.

'Marvellous,' I added. 'There's nothing quite like a bit of prostration after a day at the office. Perhaps when we actually do it on Good Friday we could do a few press-ups while we're down there.'

Canon George looked at me over the top of his glasses, and Stephen laughed before saying:

'Look, I'm sorry to hurry things along, but I'm seeing Rosie Blatch about her wedding at seven thirty. Do you think we could move on?'

Canon George said that of course we could, and, dusting himself down, he proceeded to talk us through the remainder of the Good Friday afternoon liturgy. By twenty past seven we had finished our run-through. Stephen dashed off to visit Rosie Blatch, and Canon George drove me home in his car.

As we were leaving St John's, and during the journey home, Canon George told me about a strange man who had been hanging around St Mary's for the last few days.

'His name, as I now gather, is Josh. He's one of those people that it's difficult to put an age to. I suppose he's in his thirties. Tall, willowy, scrawny really. High cheek bones, long matted hair and a grubby beard. Clearly he's been sleeping rough for quite a time. Seems very philosophical about it in a way. But what surprises me is that I've not seen him before.'

'Why does that surprise you?' I said. 'Surely someone like that is always moving on from one place to the next.'

'Well, you would think so. But it doesn't tend to

happen that way around here. Probably because we're not exactly on the way to *anywhere* much. The folk I have calling at the vicarage for alms or something to eat are quite often familiar characters. Even if I haven't seen them for some time. But Josh is different. There's something quite new and odd about him.'

'What do you mean?'

'I'm not sure,' said Canon George thoughtfully. 'It's almost as if he knows something that we don't.'

'What sort of thing?'

'Oh, I don't know. It's silly really. It's just a feeling I have when I look into his eyes.'

'It sounds as if you've struck up something of a close relationship.'

'Yes, I suppose it must sound like that. Hm.'

Canon George was quiet for a while, and then he continued where he had left off.

'His eyes. Yes. His eyes. He looks very tired, but his eyes sparkle. I was wondering whether perhaps he was dying.'

'More than the rest of us are, you mean?'

My remark was not meant as a joke, and Canon George did not take it as one.

'Yes, Michael. Just that. Yes. That way of putting it sums it up just right. He *does* look like he's dying more than the rest of us. Perhaps because he's been *living* more than the rest of us. Does that make any sense?'

'Yes,' I said. But I thought 'I'm not sure'.

Canon George went on.

'He was there this morning. Sitting, squatting really, on one of the flat gravestones as I went up through the churchyard to say morning prayer. And I said to him, "You look tired. Have you slept?" And do you know what he said?'

I remained silent, not feeling that a response was necessary.

'He said,' continued Canon George, '"I could sleep for days. I could sleep for days, and probably will. If I find a place to lay my head. But not now. Now is the time to keep awake." Then he crossed his legs and closed his eyes, as if in meditation.'

We had pulled up in front of my house and I waited for Canon George to conclude his story. But it seemed as if there was no more to tell.

'Right. There you are,' he said breezily. 'I'll see you tomorrow evening, then, for the Maundy Thursday service.'

I thanked him for the lift and went indoors where I poured myself and Cheryl a couple of stiff orange juices to celebrate my first prostration as a practising Christian.

* * *

When I woke on Good Friday I quickly rehearsed in my mind the programme for the day.

First I was to meet Canon George at the vicarage to help him with his cross. Then I was to go to the Good Friday Workshop being run at St Mary's for the children of the parish. Then I was to go down the hill to St John's for the Liturgy of the Cross. Then finally I was to come back up the hill to help Frank Foster move some furniture. We had used a large table as a 'forward altar' for the Maundy Thursday service, and now it had to be returned to its normal storage place, in the crypt under the church.

I took Cheryl a cup of tea in bed, had a hurried breakfast, kissed Amy on the head, and impetuously decided to cycle to St Mary's on such a beautifully clear morning.

One of the local Christian events on Good Friday was the March of Witness. This was always an ecumenical affair, drawing support from most of the local churches, and Canon George had always made a point of attending. Indeed, his presence was considered to be an absolute necessity as he always brought with him a large wooden cross that stood about eight feet high and four feet across. The cross was, of course, far too bulky and heavy for one person to carry, and so Canon George would convey it by car or van to the meeting place for the march, from where it would be transported by a medley of enthusiastic youths on its three-mile journey around the local shopping centre and adjacent suburbs. On this particular Good Friday I had agreed to help Canon George move the cross from the vicarage garage and onto the roof rack of his car.

I was just wheeling my bicycle across the path of the churchyard when I heard a voice hailing me from behind the old yew tree.

'Good morning, fellow traveller,' it said. 'Who are you looking for?'

I looked round and saw a lank and haggard man squinting at me in a knowing way. I decided to ignore his apparently lofty tone, for this (I presumed) was Josh.

'I'm not looking for anyone,' I said.

'Ah, well, you see, that's your trouble,' said Josh. 'If you're not looking for anyone, you won't find anyone. You should always be looking.'

'Right,' I said noncommittally. 'Thanks. If you'll excuse me.'

And with that I pushed on, leaving Josh to look at

life from his somewhat detached position among the graves. When I reached the gravel path in front of the vicarage I saw Canon George, dressed as usual in his cassock, struggling with a length of rope which he was attempting to lash to one side of his roof rack.

'Morning,' I called, as I parked my bicycle just inside the garage. 'I think I've just met your enigmatic friend. Yes, I agree with you. He certainly looks as if he could do with a sleep. And a bath wouldn't go amiss either.'

'Kay's not keen on having vagrants in the bath,' said Canon George, with a smile of innocence lighting up his pink face. 'She says the bath is sacrosanct. Even more than the bed. Not that we have vagrants in the bed.'

I wasn't sure whether Canon George was being serious or not, and so I tried to make light of it.

'Well, we all have our crosses to bear,' I remarked, nodding towards the large wooden cross that was propped up next to the garage door. 'Shall we get this one onto the roof rack, then?'

The next couple of minutes resembled something from a Laurel and Hardy film, as two bumbling clerics struggled to lift, position and then secure a large wooden cross on to the top of a car.

'Blimey,' I muttered, feeling that this was about as strong as I could allow my language to get. 'How do you *usually* do this?'

'Last year there were four of us. Frank, Stephen and one more. But they're not around this morning. So I'm afraid the burden has fallen on you, Michael.'

I grimaced in recognition of the honour.

'Picking it up is usually quite easy,' continued

Canon George. 'It's just getting it onto the roof rack and tying it up that's the problem.'

'You don't say!' I opined as I tried to remember something about knots from my long lost and mis-spent Scouting youth. After some minutes, when I had inflicted several hybrid sheepshanking grannies on the piece of rope, Canon George and I reassured each other that the wooden cross was securely fastened to the top of the car. Despite my display of unalloyed confidence, however, I made sure that I stepped well back as the Canon climbed into the vehicle and juddered out of the vicarage drive on his way to witness.

I waved him off, closed the garage door and made my way back up to the church to get myself ready for the Good Friday Workshop. I went quickly back up the path that led to the church, offering no more than an awkward salute to the strange figure of Josh who was still keeping guard over the graves like a kind of sentry.

* * *

The Good Friday Workshop was an annual feature at St Mary's. It took place from half past nine in the morning to half past twelve in the afternoon and involved about eighty local children between the ages of five and eleven. Each year there was a differ-ent theme for the day, and the children were put into groups to work on pictures, models and other creative outpourings under the guidance and supervision of a team of Workshop leaders. The whole event was something of an extended Sunday School, with the group sessions being punctuated by other distractions, including songs, drama and refreshments.

My own role in this arena of creativity was simply

to be the resident dog collar. I had no particular skills or qualifications for dealing with children, but was nevertheless entrusted with a whistle and a copy of the draft agenda so that I could wave my arms about at appropriate moments in an effort to direct operations in the church.

At half past nine, among the mêlée of expectant children, I could see Cheryl and Amy arriving, armed with two carrier bags of cardboard cartons, egg boxes, and other pieces of creative raw material. The theme for the Workshop was 'T.G.I.F.'. When I had first suggested this at a clergy staff meeting it had been met with a blank look from Canon George. Fortunately Stephen stepped in quickly to reassure the vicar that many young people would recognize the thought behind the letters. Thank God It's Friday.

The Workshop progressed with its usual blend of jollity and organized bedlam until a quarter to eleven. This was to be my first real opportunity to blow the whistle. I gave a startlingly long and loud blast, and then found, to my amazement, that most of the small faces had turned towards me, their eyes full of either fear or disbelief. One or two more sensitive souls did, in fact, begin to cry, and Mary West (who had been in charge of lapel badges) gave me one of her cross looks.

'Right, everyone,' I yelled in a friendly way. 'Hot cross bun time!'

I was about to direct everyone to the church hall where some of the ladies of the parish had laid out vast quantities of buns and orange juice, but my words were lost in the sound of tiny feet stampeding out through the back door and into the churchyard. Never had I seen the church empty so fast. Even the dash at the end of Sunday afternoon baptisms to avoid the 'retiring collection' at the door was as nothing compared to the abrupt exodus caused by my announcement of buns.

When I arrived at the hall, which was about twenty yards away from the main church entrance, the place was seething with small bodies. I was wending my way carefully through the heaving mass of bun-stuffing creatives when I felt a tugging at my shirt sleeve. Looking down I found Amy and a friend mouthing something at me.

'Hang on a minute,' I said, trying to lead them both into a quiet corner where I could hear what they were saying.

'This is Melanie,' said Amy. 'She's my friend.'

'Good,' I said. 'Hello, Melanie.'

Melanie pursed her lips and screwed up her eyes in what I took to be a smile.

'I told Melanie you're in charge,' Amy said seriously.

'Thanks a lot,' I replied, looking round at the mayhem that was being marshalled into some kind of order for a rendition of 'Old MacDonald'.

'Are you going to sing with the others?' I asked.

'We want to ask you something first,' said Amy.

'And what's that?'

'We saw a man outside sitting on the grass by the gravestones and wondered if he wanted a bun,' said Amy. 'Melanie said he might be something to do with God, seeing as he's next to the church. Can we give him a bun?'

I must have looked doubtful, because Amy immediately asked again in an imploring tone:

'Oh, please, Daddy. If he's something to do with God he might like a bun.'

I smiled down at her innocence and thoughtful-

ness, suddenly conscious of my own suspicion and
mean-spiritedness.

'Come on,' I said, taking each of them by the
hand. 'Don't disturb the others while they're
singing. Let's pick up a bun on the way out.'

We made our way back around two sides of the
hall, while the assembled throng struck up with
'Old MacDonald'. As we moved past the table
where the remainder of the goodies were piled.
Amy picked up a bun and the three of us walked out
into the cool air of the churchyard.

I thought we might have to spend some time
looking for Josh, but he was there, about twenty feet
away, with his back against one of the tombstones.

'They're playing my song,' he said jovially, with a
toss of his weather-beaten head. Still holding hands,
we approached where he was sitting.

'Josh MacDonald is a name I've been known by. But you can call me "Old" if you like!' His laugh was like a sudden and coarse rasping noise, and I could feel the grips of the two girls' hands tighten with a combination of fear and fascination.

'We've brought you something,' I said.

Amy held out the bun as far away from her as she could. Josh, seeing the concern in her face, moved very slowly and deliberately towards her, stopping at a point where he could reach out and take the bun from her without touching her hand.

'Thank you,' he said. 'Thank you very much. This means more to me,' he continued, showing us the bun in the sunlight, 'than you can know. Thank you.'

He held the bun out at arm's length, broke it carefully in half, and began to eat. And as he ate, he nodded his delight at the two young faces that peered at him as if he were something that had dropped from the sky.

'Well, we'd better get back to work,' I said. 'Come on, you two. Say goodbye to Mr MacDonald.'

Amy said goodbye and Melanie screwed up her face into something of a smile, and the three of us turned and traced our steps back to the church. By this time the rest of the children and helpers were also filing back in. The two girls were about to resume their places in a group that was painting large faces onto the back of a roll of wallpaper, when Amy turned to me and said:

'Is his name *really* Mr MacDonald?'

'I don't know,' I said truthfully. 'Why do you ask?'

'Oh, I just wondered if he was part of the family of the man who owns all the burger shops.'

'He *could* be,' I said, again truthfully. I then added, rather lamely, 'in the end we're all part of the same family.'

163

'Oh dear,' I thought. That really *did* sound like something straight out of Sunday School. It was clear that Amy felt much the same thing. She looked up at me suspiciously and said 'I guess so' before turning away to find her paintbrush.

* * *

When the Workshop had finished I gathered my things together to walk down the road to St John's. It was nearly one o'clock when I finally left St Mary's, and so I had already missed the first part of the two hours of prayers, addresses and music that preceded the Liturgy of the Cross which began at two.

It seemed a long time since I had eaten the hot cross bun, and so I called into a café along the high street for a sandwich and a glass of milk. From there I went directly to St John's where I changed into my cassock-alb and stole, before slipping into my place while the choir was singing an anthem.

There was another forty minutes or so of music and meditation before the liturgy itself began, and by two o'clock I was feeling rather sleepy. I therefore shifted about in my place, trying to keep myself awake before preparing for the opening prostration.

The act of worship went off smoothly enough — if 'smoothly' is a word that can be used of the deep emotions occasioned by a Good Friday service in a 'high church' tradition. Canon George, Stephen and I all threw ourselves to the floor much as we had planned. I paraded a wooden cross through the church. The assembled company venerated the cross with a mixture of dignity and desperation. Finally I found myself coping for the first time with a humeral veil draped around my shoulders as I was ushered into position to bring the reserved sacrament to the altar.

By three o'clock the service was over and I was feeling physically and emotionally drained. There was still, however, one job that needed doing before I could return home to my family. I had arranged to meet Frank Foster back at St Mary's as soon after three as possible. By then the clearing up operation after the Workshop would have finished, and Frank wanted some help in taking apart and storing the large table that we had used the previous evening as a forward altar.

When I arrived at St Mary's Frank had already begun to dismantle the table, and between us we carried the various parts to the back of the church and the entrance to the crypt. The crypt at St Mary's consisted of a chain of linked cellular recesses along both sides of a subterranean channel that ran the length of the church. Most of the recesses were occupied by various bits of furniture or packing cases, but a few were vacant, or housed individual items like the Christmas crib scene.

Access to the crypt was through a large sliding trap door in the floor of the church, which Frank unlocked and unbolted when we had collected together the sections of the table. With Frank standing at the bottom of the small flight of six or seven steps, and me standing above him handing down the legs and then the leaves, we began to stow the table away.

It was then that we heard the familiar voice of Canon George calling to us from just inside the church porch.

'Ah, wonderful!' he cried. 'The Lord has answered my prayers.'

'So what does *that* mean you're after?' said Frank cynically, popping his head out from below the level of the floor.

Canon George walked over to where I was standing staring down at Frank.

'Two able-bodied men. That is what the Lord has sent me!' chuckled Canon George. 'When I came back from the march of witness this morning, I didn't have time to unload the cross before I had to get down to St John's. I was hoping that you might be able to help me take it down from the roof rack and back into the garage. Kay needs the car.'

Frank clambered up the steps.

'Come on, then,' he said. 'Let's do that right away, and then we'll finish stowing the table. All right, Michael?'

'Of course,' I said, and the three of us headed back towards the main door of the church.

'Better lock up,' said Frank. 'I know we'll only be away for a couple of minutes, but we don't want anyone wandering into the church and falling down the hole into the crypt, do we?'

'Indeed not,' said Canon George, locking the door behind us.

With three of us, it took no time at all to untie the cross and carry it across the vicarage drive and into the garage which Canon George had opened earlier. Within a few minutes, we were all heading back to the church to finish the job of storing the table in the crypt. Once inside, Frank again took up his position at the foot of the steps, and Canon George and I handed him down the remaining sections of table.

'Well, that's a job well done,' said Frank, pulling the sliding door back across the opening, and locking and bolting it into position. 'What's next?'

'A well deserved drink, I think,' said Canon George. 'Would you both like to come back to the vicarage for a glass of something fortifying?'

'Not for me, thanks,' I said. 'Only one and a half more days and you can give me as much fortifying drink as you like. But not now, thanks all the same. I feel as if I've been away from the house for ages. So I'll head for home, if you don't mind.'

'Of course not, Michael. You *have* been here since about eight this morning. Cheryl and Amy will be missing you. Go on, you get going.'

'Thanks. I'll come back to the vicarage with you to get my bike. You remember, I left it in your garage.'

As I said this I was suddenly aware that I didn't remember seeing the bicycle when we had been moving the wooden cross only minutes before. It wasn't, therefore, a complete shock when I peered into the garage and saw no sign of it anywhere.

'Gone,' I said simply.

Canon George held his head in his hands.

'Oh, I'm so dreadfully sorry,' he said. 'I shouldn't have left the garage door open when I came up to find you. It's just that, usually, there's never anything in there worth taking. Oh, I'm so sorry, Michael. We'll have to find you another one somehow.'

I made a series of comments to the effect that it didn't matter; that I rarely used it; that it wasn't worth much. But, even so, the theft — if theft it was — niggled me.

'Bloomin' kids,' said Frank in a low growl. 'You can't leave anything around these days.'

'I'm not sure,' I said quietly. For the picture I had in my mind was not of 'kids', but rather that of a long-haired and bearded man with a twinkle in his eye.

167

Going under

When Jesus arrived he found that Lazarus
had already been in the tomb four days.
(John 11:17)

WHEN I arrived home from St Mary's on Good
Friday afternoon, Cheryl told me that Chris
Mulligan had phoned an hour or so earlier. He had
left a message asking me to call him back at what I
assumed was his home number. After the events of
the day I did not want to be reminded of work. I had
left the office on Maundy Thursday looking forward
to a four-day break from advertising, although I
knew that the long weekend would hardly be a
holiday. The last thing I wanted was Chris Mulligan
ringing to talk about Pronto Pizzas.

'I thought that clients weren't supposed to have
your home phone number,' said Cheryl.

'They're not,' I said, remembering the scene at
Rome airport. 'I must have given it to him in a weak
moment.'

Weak moment or not, it suddenly dawned on me
that Mulligan might be ringing about a personal
matter.

'I'd better get back to him,' I said quickly.

'What's the rush?' said Cheryl. 'Sit down and
have a cup of tea first.'

'No, it's OK,' I replied. 'I'd rather get this out of
the way.'

The phone rang for a long time before I heard

Mulligan's gruff voice at the other end. He sounded oddly mellow and as if he had been drinking. True to form, however, he did not beat about the bush. He told me without any ceremony that his wife had left him on Wednesday morning and taken the children to stay with friends in Milton Keynes. Could we talk? Could I meet him the next day in London? I was the only person he could talk to, and he needed to sort some things out in his head. I'd told him that it was all right to ring, hadn't I? Where could we meet?

The combination of urgency and matter-of-factness in his voice swept me along. I found that I was being given no opportunity to register any opinion or objection to the plan that Mulligan had clearly already hatched. Perhaps it was simply that I felt weak after the activities and emotions of the day. I felt sure that it was my tiredness rather than any real pastoral sensitivity that fashioned my response.

When later I reflected on the conversation, I was annoyed at myself for not being more assertive. By nightfall, however, any resentment had turned to a more positive feeling of interest, or perhaps even simple curiosity. As it happened, Cheryl and I had made no plans to do anything much the next day, Easter Saturday. Amy was going to a friend's birthday party in the afternoon, and I had intended to spend the day slobbing around the house pretending to do the sorts of things that I had been promising to do for months. Clearing out the garage, ironing the clothes that had taken up permanent residence at the bottom of the washing basket. That sort of thing.

Ultimately, therefore, it was with no great sense of sacrifice that I arranged to meet Mulligan under the big clock on Waterloo Station at eleven o'clock the next morning.

Mulligan had suggested meeting in London because he intended spending the first part of this Saturday morning at the Pronto Pizza offices which were in Vauxhall. When I arrived at Waterloo at 10.55 he was already standing under the clock. He was dressed casually in light brown chinos, blue sweater and Barbour, but still managed to look awkwardly formal and furtive, full of impatience and as if he would rather be anywhere else. When he saw me approaching, however, he assumed his usual bluff exterior, grinned at me with his uneven teeth, and held out his hand in welcome.

'Michael,' he announced. 'Good to see you. Thanks for coming. Hope you don't mind. You *did* say. You know. To give you a call, I mean. I'm sure you'd rather be . . . Well, there we are. Thanks all the same.'

The words tumbled out in a way that suggested he had been there for some time thinking about what he would say to open the conversation. When the flow finally stopped he looked at me, the grin still fixed on his face. It was my turn to take the initiative.

'Do you want to go anywhere in particular?' I asked.

'Nowhere,' said Mulligan, shrugging and beginning to look helpless.

'Well, it's a beautiful day,' I said. 'How about a walk along the river?'

'I thought it was only your boss who walked on water,' he quipped, slapping me on the shoulder and beginning to walk by my side.

I smiled at him and wondered how he was going

to handle this meeting. Not being the boss, the manager. The roles on this occasion were going to be different from usual. But then he must know that. Still, I was glad that he felt able to show something of his usual bluff self. It was probably a mask, but it might also be a way of helping him to relax.

We turned to leave the station concourse, walking past the international terminal for the Channel Tunnel trains. As we passed along the foot-bridge over the road and through the Shell Centre, Mulligan spoke mainly about matters related to work. Down we went, towards the Royal Festival Hall, past the bust of Nelson Mandela and on to the riverside walkway heading east towards Blackfriars and the City of London.

Once we were next to the river, Mulligan's mood changed. He pushed his hands deep into the pockets of his Barbour and hunched his shoulders against the sharp wind that seemed to be whipping off the glistening water and bouncing back from the concrete blocks of the South Bank.

'I've made a real mess of things, haven't I?' he said into the wind.

'I don't know, Chris. Have you?'

'For God's sake, Michael!'

Mulligan sighed and stopped by a concrete pillar, turning his head away from the wind and cupping his hands whilst he lit a cigarette.

'I'm sorry,' he breathed out with the smoke. 'I'm a bit tense. It was good of you to come. Giving up time with your family.'

'They're busy today, as it happens. Look, Chris, you'll have to *tell* me. I don't actually know what's happened. Tell me just as much as you want to. A bit further on there's a place where we can get some coffee. I'm very happy to listen to whatever you've got to say.'

My words, clumsy as they may have been, served to open the floodgates. Without further ado Mulligan unloaded on me what I took to be most of the story. It was a story related in a dull flat tone, with little indication at any point of what his real feelings may have been.

Extramarital affairs had become something of a habit. There had now been three 'little flings' over an eight-year period. They had all arisen in the context of work. The liaisons had all consisted of not much more than occasional couplings in hotel rooms. They had, however, become something of a surrogate for any relationship that Mulligan might have had with his wife, Anne.

Anne had been very hurt to begin with. She may have guessed about her husband's first affair. She found out about the second. He had told her about the third. By then she had already begun to think in terms of her own life and the futures of her two daughters, Claire and Rebecca.

Mulligan's unabashed retelling of his latest sexual exploits, brought on by an excess of alcohol (and what I felt was probably an instinctive spitefulness), had been the last straw.

The Marketing Manager for Pronto Pizzas had returned home from work on Wednesday to find that his wife and children had decamped with most of their clothes and personal effects to stay with Anne's best friend and her husband.

'She took the Volvo, and I reckon she must have just about filled it with all their stuff. It was certainly more than a suitcase job. Which is why I think they've gone for good.'

By now we were sitting drinking coffee at Gabriel's Wharf.

'And so now you're on your own,' I said, stating the obvious.

'Too right!'

I waved away his offer of a cigarette. He always offered, I always waved the offer away.

'Chris, what are you upset about exactly? Is it the breakdown of the marriage? Is it the children?'

I knew as I spoke that it was a somewhat insensitive question. Mulligan seemed not to mind my brusque approach. He swallowed hard and looked away from me.

'The kids. I've really screwed it up for the kids, haven't I? And they must think I'm a right bastard. And yet I love them so much. I really do. And I've lost them. I've lost them.'

There was a pause.

'And Anne,' I prompted as gently as I could. 'Do you think you've lost her as well?'

'Anne?' he mused, as if I had introduced a completely different subject. 'She didn't deserve this.'

'This?'

'Me, I mean. She deserved better than me. I don't blame her. I would have done the same.'

I couldn't help smiling at him, and at the suggestion that Anne was blameless because she had acted as her husband would have done.

'Have you tried to see it, the situation, from Anne's point of view?'

'Of course I have,' Mulligan said sharply. 'What do you think I am? I told you. I would have done the same thing. I was wrong, I know that. I shouldn't have played around. And now she's gone.

173

And I'm left on my own trying to work out what to do.'

'To get her to come back?'

'I don't know. She probably doesn't want to come back.'

'Have you asked her?'

Mulligan looked at me as if I had suggested something out of this world.

'*Asked* her?'

'Have you spoken to her, I mean? Since she left?'

'Of course not,' said Mulligan incredulously. 'What's the point?'

'You've got her number,' I said. 'The friend she's staying with?'

Mulligan lit another cigarette.

'Look, she's left me. There's nothing to talk about. If there had been anything to talk about we would have talked. Before, I mean.'

By now we had resumed our walk along by the river.

'*Would* you have done?' I persisted.

'What?'

'Talked.'

'Of course. I'm a great talker.'

'Yes,' I said dejectedly. 'I believe you are, Chris.'

As we arrived at the side of Blackfriars Bridge I nodded towards the steps that led up to the road.

'We'll have to cross over before we can get back down to the river-front.'

'Hang on a minute,' said Mulligan, peering over the edge of the stonework at the water below. 'Look, it's low tide. I bet you we could get through under the bridge.'

I must have looked doubtful as I approached where he was standing.

'Come on,' he said, recapturing something of his usual confidence. 'Where's your sense of adventure? Come on! Follow me!'

Without further ado he made his way down the stone steps and onto the narrow strand of pebbles that was being lapped by the dirty water of the Thames.

'We can get through underneath,' he called back up to me. 'Come on, Michael, I can see a clear way through.'

Mainly, I am sure, out of some sense of solidarity, I followed him down the steps and onto the shingle. For some reason I felt nervous. It wasn't that I was afraid of the Thames, licking at the stones only inches from where I was standing. It was more to do with the apparent flouting of authority or normality. I wasn't sure whether what we were doing was *allowed*. Whether there was any law preventing us from acting like this, or whether it was a perfectly acceptable right of way. The feeling in the pit of my stomach was like the kind of feeling I used to experience as a ten-year-old, climbing into someone's garden without permission to retrieve a lost ball.

It was a feeling that made me uncomfortable. I felt as if I were being led astray by one of the naughty boys. That by walking under the bridge I was somehow going against the accepted rules of adult conduct.

I was keen to get moving and to emerge on the other side quickly. I wasn't even sure that there would be a means for us to get back up to the path on the far side of the bridge. I imagined us having to retrace our steps, only to cross the road as I had first suggested.

Mulligan, however, seemed strangely at ease

standing below the stonework of Blackfriars Bridge, smoking thoughtfully and letting the seamy water almost touch the toes of his shoes.

'Right,' I said, trying to inject a note of urgency into the proceedings. 'Let's get moving before the tide comes in.'

'What's the hurry?' Mulligan said. 'I rather like it down here. What's that they say? Far from the maddening crowd, eh?'

'It's madding,' I said. 'Madding crowd.' I could feel myself beginning to get irritable. 'Well, I'm not sure I *do* like it down here.'

'Down under,' laughed Mulligan. 'OK. Let's move on.'

It was with some relief that we emerged on the other side of the bridge to find a flight of stone steps that led back up to the river walkway.

As we climbed back up, an elderly coupled walked by and eyed us suspiciously. I tried to look as if I had authority to be down by the river's edge, but I felt sure that my unsettledness must have shown through.

The interesting thing was, however, that Mulligan seemed to have gained confidence from the excursion.

'I know what you're thinking,' he said when we resumed our walk, as if there had been no break in our conversation.

'You do?' I said, not even sure myself what I had been thinking.

'You're thinking "If he doesn't want advice on how to get his wife back, then why did he want to see me?" Am I right?'

I smiled back bleakly at Mulligan. I was fairly sure that I had been thinking nothing of the kind, but I wanted to see where his train of thought was going.

'Well, I'll tell you,' he continued. 'When I got home three days ago and found they'd all gone, do you know what the first thing I did was?'

I didn't say anything.

'I poured myself a drink, and I sat down, and I stared at the wall. Then the doorbell rang. And do you know who it was? It was one of your lot. A Christian, from the local church. And he said to me, "I'd like to wish you and your family a Happy Easter and let you know that you'd all be very welcome at our Easter morning service on Sunday at All Saints." That's our local church. And then he said, "We'll all be there, celebrating the new life that the risen Lord has brought us. Hope to see you there too. Have a nice day", or whatever it was he said. Can you believe that? There am I, Scotch in hand, fag in mouth, wifeless, childless. And this joker says "Come and celebrate the new life that the risen Lord has brought you!" Some kind of new life, eh? Is that what your religion's about, Michael? Is it? Because if it is, you can stuff it!'

Mulligan caught himself getting indignant, stopped momentarily, and then started laughing, as if to make light of the comments he had just uttered. He looked up at a large building, the impressive shell of a power station, and said:

'Helluva lot of bricks in that!'

'Yes,' I said lamely. I wasn't sure what to say, and so filled the silence by pointing out the site of a Shakespearean theatre and a stone seat set into the side of a building. The seat had been where the ferryman had perched whilst waiting for fares to steer across the Thames below Southwark Bridge.

As we passed under a brick archway I felt that I

knew what I wanted to ask Mulligan, although I wasn't sure that it was the right question to put to him.

'Who are you angry at, Chris?'

'Angry?' he almost snarled back.

'Yes,' I continued. 'Is it me? Is it Anne? Is it God? Or . . .'

'Or what?'

'Or is it you?'

'Angry at *me*?' His eyes were as wide open as they could have been. 'Why should I be angry at myself?'

'You tell me. You started off by telling me how you thought you had made a mess of it all.'

He ignored the comment.

'It's certainly not you,' he said, trying to give me a reassuring smile. 'And I've told you I don't blame Anne.' He thought for a moment. 'I think it's God. Mind you, I'm not saying I believe in him. It. Whatever. Whatever it is that *forms* our lives. You know? That's what I've got a beef about. Fate, that's what it is. Isn't it?'

Sometimes the way Mulligan swung between extreme confidence and thinly-veiled vulnerability caught me off guard. I thought, 'He's asking me to tell him what's going on. He thinks I might know. How can I tell him that I don't know, and yet still say something that he might find helpful?'

'Well, *isn't* it?' he said again, with a note of urgency.

'You don't want me to talk to you about Jesus Christ or Easter, do you?'

He stopped momentarily before saying:

'I want you to tell me how to be happy.'

I looked quickly across at him. We were walking past the old Clink prison, now a museum, and, for a

178

second, I thought he was baiting me. But when I saw the grey skin stretched tight around his eyes, and the square jaw pushed forward in a caricature of defiance, I understood that this was a real cry for help, and I suddenly felt the burden of responsibility.

My mouth began to form an instant response, but I bit back the words and continued to walk on along the path with Mulligan silent at my side.

'Have you ever been in Southwark Cathedral?' I said at last.

'No,' said Mulligan gloomily. 'Where is it?'

I smiled and slowed my pace.

'It's here, Chris,' I said. 'It's here.'

He looked up to where the bulk of the cathedral loomed darkly above us.

'Do you want to come in and have a look?'

Mulligan had just taken out a cigarette, but he pushed it back into the packet as he said:

'Why not? What have I got to lose?'

* * *

We were sitting next to each other about halfway along the nave facing forward. There was no service in progress, and various people in small groups moved about along the aisles, or mooched at the book stalls.

'I was ordained here, Chris. Last October. This is the first time I've been here since then. It's a very special place for me.'

'Yes, I know,' said Mulligan softly. 'I could tell that from the way you suggested we came in. Like you were inviting me into your home.'

I smiled. Mulligan spoke again.

'If you want me to go off and leave you to pray or

something, that's OK by me. I'll see you outside later.'

'No, Chris,' I said quickly. 'I don't want to pray.'

We sat in silence for a few moments before I said:

'Chris, just now you said something very . . . Well, very sensitive. About the cathedral being like my home.'

'So?'

'So why can't you be like that more often?'

'What? Sensitive? I guess I'm just not a sensitive sort of bloke.'

'No, that's not what I mean. Every now and again you let yourself go. You respond to what's going on around you. To what people are thinking inside. You let something that's in you get out. It's a sort of thoughtfulness. But most of the time you keep it chained up inside a prison. A prison that is the *rest* of you. The bluff, tough manager who can't accept that anything is unmanageable. Like that time in Rome when you let me go to comfort Carol.'

'I *told* you to go,' said Mulligan.

'Yes, you did, didn't you?' I said with a laugh. 'So even *then* you had to be in control. And that's just what I mean. When I came here last October to be ordained, I thought I was being given a share in trying to manage this crazy organization that is the church. I think I've learned a lot in the last six months, and one of the things I've learned is that management is a myth. That's not to say we shouldn't all strive to do things better. To organize things better. Goodness knows, the church could learn a lot in that area. But the important thing is that you have to begin by being open to the creative possibilities around you. You can't begin by burying yourself under a pile of self-imposed limitations.'

I was conscious that I was getting 'heavy', and so I attempted to lighten the tone.

'Basically, Chris, I think you have to be able to laugh at yourself and all those around you before you can hope to see any sense in it. If you can embrace chaos, you might just see past the nonsense. And then you might find peace. How's that, then , for a lecture on the philosophy of life?'

I thought Mulligan might have had enough of my wittering, but he was looking at me and smiling for the first time since we had entered the cathedral.

'Well, I think,' he said, 'that there's a lot in that. You're not as silly as you look, Michael! Sometimes you talk good sense. But you have to admit, it's nothing to do with Christianity — and I thought you would have tried a bit of the old evangelism on me. What with you playing at home, as it were, and me being very much part of the away team.'

We both rose from our seats at the same time and began a slow perambulation around the building, stopping every now and again to read the inscriptions in a half-interested way.

'I suppose I *was* making a bit of a statement in a way,' I said, not wanting to feel that my Christianity and my assumed good sense should be seen to be at odds.

'When I say "peace" I guess I mean "God",' I said. 'How does that sound?'

'I thought God was supposed to be a person.'

'No. Jesus was a person.'

'But you think he was the same as God, don't you?'

'I'm not sure I do,' I said honestly.

'Not sure? But where does that leave your Christianity if you're not sure? The people who

181

built *this* place must have been pretty sure. If there's one thing that all this stone, all these windows, all this gold, says it's "I am sure!" So what business have you got to be ordained if you're not sure? What's faith, Michael, if it's not based on certainty and sureness?'

'But that's just it, Chris. Faith is faith. If there were anything certain about it, it would not be faith. It would simply be agreeing to something that was patently obvious. Faith isn't that simple. Life isn't that simple.'

'You're telling me!' said Chris gruffly, although he was still smiling. 'Come on, let's get out of here. The way you talk makes me think that this whole place might collapse about my ears any minute.'

As we left the cathedral I was conscious that I had raised many more questions than I had supplied answers, and I wondered what Mulligan had made of it all. He seemed at first not to be interested in pursuing this line of conversation once we were back out in the crisp air.

'I know where we are,' he said breezily. 'This is London Bridge, isn't it? I've never come to it this way before. Southwark Cathedral falling about my ears. London Bridge falling down. The collapse of my marriage. It's all of a piece really, don't you think? A world where things fall apart. And that's just *me*. What about Bosnia? What about famine in Africa? What about all that crap going on out there?' He waved his arm expansively towards the rest of London before continuing. 'I'm not sure I want to embrace that kind of chaos. Those sorts of creative possibilities. They sound far too dangerous.'

He laughed before saying:

'You see? I *was* listening to your sermon, Vicar.

But I guess I'm one of life's prisoners, after all. Me and most of the rest of the human beings on this planet. Come on, Michael. Loosen up. I'm only kidding.'

He slapped me heartily on the back.

'Come on,' he said. 'The London Dungeon's near here, and I've never been. Anne said the girls were too young last time we were up this way. Do you fancy a visit?'

The last thing I wanted to do on an Easter Saturday was to visit the London Dungeon, but I still felt that I owed it to Mulligan to stay with him. That odd sense of loyalty meant that I spent the next hour wandering around in a damp, dark cavernous place looking at grotesque life-size wax models of people being tortured and killed in all manner of horrific circumstances. Mulligan spent most of the time in silence, reading the inscriptions for each of the tableaux. Occasionally he guffawed and pointed incredulously at some horrendous depiction of agony.

Finally, as we left, he nudged me heavily in the ribs and said:

'See what I mean?'

I stared back at him.

'Creative possibilities, Michael. Creative possibilities. *That's* what people do to each other,' he said, flicking his head back towards the depths from which we had just emerged.

'Look,' I replied, feeling for the first time that Mulligan might think that I was deluding myself. 'I'm not saying it doesn't exist. Suffering, I mean. It really doesn't require much of a journey for any of us to descend into some kind of hell. But there *is* a better way. It's a way that I associate with Jesus

183

Christ. That way doesn't take *away* the darkness. But it does give us a light so that we can see where the darkness is. Resurrection doesn't cancel out crucifixion. But it gives us hope. You're down now, Chris. Of course you are. But please try to let some of the light in. And look around you.'

We were standing on London Bridge looking down towards H.M.S. *Belfast*. Mulligan suddenly turned to me and said:

'Have you ever done a funeral, Michael?'

'Just one,' I answered, remembering my excursion to the Roman Catholic cemetery.

'And what did you tell the relatives of the deceased? Did you say that their beloved had gone to heaven or to hell?'

'I don't think they asked me,' I said truthfully.

'Let you off the hook, eh?' smiled Mulligan. 'Well, I won't be so polite. What do you reckon about me, then? Will I go to heaven or to hell?'

I did not know what kind of answer he was expecting.

'I think heaven starts now. If we let it. By being open to God. Some kind of spiritual openness that then goes beyond the grave,' I said at last.

'Hmph!' grunted Mulligan. 'And hell? Does that start now as well?'

'I think it begins in being closed. By being cut off. From God, I mean. And from, yes, the creative possibilities that are part of that divinity. So that death really is death. The end.'

Mulligan frisked himself, looking for his cigarettes.

'Listen, Michael,' he said. 'You're a good guy. I really do appreciate your coming up here to meet me. To listen to me and to talk to me. You haven't once tried to tell me that Jesus loves me or that Jesus will save me. And that's cool.'

He found the cigarettes and lit one.

'But one day, my friend, when I'm more myself, I'm going to interrogate that faith of yours. You see, it seems to me that it's either all plain common sense, and we should all believe in it, or the silent majority of heathens are right after all, and it's all a load of rubbish. And you don't need to look so concerned. Before today, before these last three or four days, I thought I knew what I believed. Now? Well, now I'm not so sure. There's something about what you stand for, Michael, that's . . . Well, I don't know. But at least I'm listening, so perhaps you can count that as a success, Mr Clergyman.'

I laughed nervously, hoping against hope that some of the light might illuminate some of Mulligan's darkness.

'And Anne?' I suggested quietly.

'We'll talk. At least I hope we will. That is, I'll phone her when I get home.'

Mulligan held out his hand abruptly and I realized that our meeting was over.

'You get back to your family,' he said with a grin. 'Otherwise you'll be in for a deal of marital strife yourself. I'll talk to you next week. Let you know how things are.'

Before I had even a chance to say something supportive he was striding away across the bridge towards the City, his shoulders once more hunched against the wind. I turned the other way, wincing at the taste of exhaust fumes. Wanting to be at home, and thinking of Easter.

* * *

When I returned home Cheryl said that Frank Foster had phoned. He had recovered my bicycle. He had seen some kids playing with it on the waste ground close to St Mary's. They had scarpered when he had challenged them, leaving the bicycle behind. It was now safely locked away back in the vicarage garage again. I had no need to worry, he had said.

Except that I did worry. About Cheryl and Amy. About my ministry. About Chris Mulligan and his family. Even about Josh MacDonald, whom I had wrongly assumed to be the bicycle thief.

That night I lay in the dark with a muddled mind, praying for resurrection.

ELEVEN

Knock, knock, who's there?

And remember, I am with you always, to the end of the age. (Matthew 28:20)

EASTER morning. Early. The daylight still no more than a faint glow where the rooftops meet the sky. No sounds, except the deep breathing of Cheryl who lay next to me in bed, mostly hidden beneath a capacious quilt. No sounds, except that something had woken me. There must have been another sound.

I lay quite still for a few seconds and then heard it again. A low, quiet knocking, coming from downstairs. Coming, it seemed, from the front door.

I climbed out of bed and slid stealthily into my dressing gown and slippers. Down the stairs warily. Into the hallway, where I felt I could risk switching on a light.

And there it was again. A low, soft, almost apologetic knock, knock, knock on the front door. I leaned forward and said in a voice that I hoped would not wake Cheryl or Amy:

'Who's there?'

'It's me,' came the reply. 'Martha.'

I immediately unbolted the door to find Martha Cummings waiting, fully dressed, on the step. I hadn't seen much of her since her father's funeral, and now I feared the worst.

'What's the matter, Martha?' I enquired earnestly. 'What on earth is the matter? What's happened?'

Martha did not answer my questions directly. She

seemed more concerned to apologize for waking me.

'I'm sorry to have got you up, Michael,' she said. 'But I thought you might be awake, it being Easter Day and all that. I tried to knock very quietly.'

'It's all right, Martha. I was just about to get up,' I lied. 'We're not having a very early service at St Mary's this year. The first one is at eight o-clock and the vicar's doing that on his own. I'm on with him at nine thirty. Come in out of the cold and tell me what's happened.'

She stepped quickly into the hallway, looking behind her as if to make sure she hadn't disturbed the whole street.

'I'll come right to the point,' she said. I remembered the last occasion on which Martha had 'come right to the point' and allowed myself a smile. Much to my surprise, however, she *did* come right to the point.

'It's Maria,' she said.

'Your pregnant lodger,' I chipped in.

'Well, that's just it,' went on Martha. 'She's about to have it. The baby, I mean. If I know anything at all about these things, she's about to have it. Very soon too. So I thought we'd better get her to the hospital as quickly as possible. Which is why I'm here, you see. I'm ever so sorry to impose on you again, Michael. But Maria, poor love, can't drive in the state she's in. And, as I said, I thought you might be up already.'

Martha's news came as a great relief. I thought she had been about to tell me of some tragedy or death and, although the idea of Maria's plight was not yet something to celebrate, it cheered me enormously. I had never enquired about the whereabouts of the father, and felt that this was not the moment to raise the issue.

'Yes, of course,' I blurted out. 'You go back and look after her. I'll throw some clothes on and then bring the car round to pick the two of you up. I'll be no more than five minutes.'

With that Martha crept back out of the house, and I made my way upstairs to wake Cheryl so that I could tell her what was happening.

I looked at the clock. It was twenty past five. I pulled on some trousers, struggled into a sweat shirt, and pushed my feet into a pair of moccasins. I picked up some money from the cabinet next to the bed and stuffed it into my back pocket. I craned forward to stare at my stubbled chin and unkempt hair in the bathroom mirror. That would all have to wait. There would be time for that later.

Back in the bedroom I leaned over Cheryl's bed-warm body and shook her gently. When her eyes finally opened and fastened on mine, I started to speak.

'I'm just taking Maria and Martha to the hospital. She's having her baby.'

'Martha?' slurred Cheryl, still not awake.

'Maria,' I countered.

'Having a baby,' repeated Cheryl, screwing up her eyes.

'Yes,' I replied, kissing her on the forehead. 'See you later.'

I briefly looked in at Amy, who was sleeping soundly, and then went downstairs and out into the chill morning air. The glow of the newborn sun was spreading in a milky haze across the lower reaches of the sky as I climbed into the car, switched on my lights and drove out of the drive and the fifty or so yards to the front of Martha's house.

Martha and Maria were waiting in the orange-lit doorway and made their way down the few steps as soon as they saw me. Maria was covered in a fur coat that I suspected belonged to Martha. She was clutching her bulging body. A look that was half anguish, half hope contorted her face. Martha had her arm around her lodger and friend, and helped her into the back of the car, before sliding in herself.

As I pulled away Maria started to speak.

'I'm so sorry,' she said. 'If he had been here, this wouldn't have happened. I'm sorry.'

'There, there,' said Martha comfortingly. 'We're nearly there.'

I wasn't sure what Maria's words had meant. 'He' was presumably the father. But whether she was blaming him for the child, or for not being there to drive her to the hospital, was unclear. Again, I reflected, now was not the time to ask. I also became conscious of how much Martha was offering to Maria. There was a tenderness about her that I had never seen before. Perhaps because I had never been in a position to see it. I looked in my mirror and saw Martha cradling Maria softly in her arms.

'Don't you worry yourself about him,' said Martha. 'Just remember, I'm with you. I'll be with you. Till we get through this. Don't you worry none.'

My mind filled up with all sorts of different thoughts. In my rear-view mirror I could see the basic compassion of one human being for another. A basic compassion that always gave me hope. Ahead of me I could see a red light. There was no traffic around. Should I drive through it? And, as the thought came into my mind, I remembered my own journey towards ordination just six months before. The time when I had been stopped by the police. Another drive in the same car with passengers in the back.

On that first occasion the passengers were ministers in the name of Jesus Christ. And on this occasion? The ministry which Martha was showing to Maria was no less a part, I felt, of God's working in the world — and in many ways it was even more, because conducted in such an anonymous and natural way.

The red light turned to green, and I was able to continue the journey without stopping and without risking the wrath of the law. By the time we reached the hospital it was a quarter to six and, as Martha and I helped Maria into the stark and angular building, the rays of the sun were beginning to weave their incandescent magic through the morning air.

For the first time that day since I had first heard the knocking on the door, I truly realized what day it was. Martha's earlier words had not sunk in. Yes, of course, Easter Day. But at the time, my mind had been more on my neighbour's plight than on the risen Lord. Now, with Maria safe in the hands of the experts, and with the sun beginning to take on its usual glory, I allowed myself to bathe in the beauty of this morning.

* * *

Martha and I sat huddled together in a bare waiting room. One other person was there. A portly man with a heavy moustache who was eating corned beef sandwiches and drinking milky coffee from a Thermos flask

Martha had, on several occasions already, told me to go home to my family. But I still felt inclined to stay. For just a bit longer. When we arrived the nurses had intimated that Maria was 'nearly there' and it was clear that the delivery was expected within a relatively short space of time.

Half an hour passed. By twenty past six the portly man had offered us some chocolate biscuits and told us that his Denise had been in labour for seventeen hours and that he was 'taking a bit of a breather'. Martha muttered quietly that she rather thought Denise would've liked a bit of a breather herself.

By a quarter to seven Martha was asleep on my shoulder, and I was beginning to feel cramped and in need of an invigorating shower. The portly man had gone outside for a cigarette. Still no word from the delivery room.

At seven o'clock the portly man gave us a wave, and left us his copy of yesterday's *Daily Express*, as he jauntily went back in to be with his wife.

I was just beginning to feel that perhaps I should return home after all, when a nurse appeared and asked for Martha. Martha woke from her half-slumber, shot to her feet and grabbed my hand tightly.

'A bouncing baby boy,' said the nurse with a big smile. 'Mother and son are looking great. Would you like to come in?'

There was a short pause, just long enough for Martha to gulp in some air while her eyes widened in delight. Then she started crying whilst she dug around in her pockets for a handkerchief.

'I gave my hanky to Maria,' she sobbed.

'Here, take mine,' I said, feeling the tears massing

behind my eyes. 'I think it's clean.'

I gave her a long hug whilst the nurse waited diplomatically by the door of the delivery rooms. I dug in my back pocket for some money.

'Here, Martha,' I said. 'Here's ten pounds. No, go on. You can owe it to me. Get yourself a cab back home when you're ready. In case I'm at church, I mean. Get yourself a cab.'

She asked me to come in to see Maria and the baby, but I told her that I really did need to be at home with my own family now.

'You're here,' I said. 'That's what matters. I heard what you said to Maria. In the car.'

Martha looked up at me quizzically.

'You said,' I went on. 'You said you would stay with Maria. All the time. Till she got through this, you said.'

She smiled and nodded.

'I'll stay,' she said. 'You go now. And give my love to your wife and daughter.'

I gave her another quick hug, and started walking towards the exit.

'And, Michael,' she called after me.

I turned around.

'Happy Easter,' she said, wiping the tears from her cheeks with my handkerchief.

I swallowed hard and walked back out into the crisp bright morning light.

* * *

Such was the pace of the morning that by eight o'clock I had returned home, shaved, showered and dressed, and was sitting at the table in the kitchen eating my Easter breakfast. Opposite me, and still in her pyjamas, Amy was wrestling with a large egg that refused to come out of its wrapping.

I had told Cheryl and Amy about what had happened already that morning, and then I began to get philosophical over the toast.

'You know,' I said, chewing thoughtfully, 'the world is full of people like Martha, all doing their bit to make the world a better place. That's what gives me hope.'

'But Martha's not a Christian,' said a smiling Cheryl, provoking me. 'Does that mean that your hope is founded on non-Christians after all?'

'You know what I mean,' I said scowling back at her.

'Well, I'm not sure I do,' said Cheryl. 'I agree with your point about the world being full of Marthas. But most of them have nothing to do with organized religion. The majority are quite happy looking after each other with varying degrees of love, without ever coming to church. Even on a day like today. How many people do you think there will be at St Mary's this morning?'

'Easter Morning? I think there were about two hundred and fifty last year,' I replied.

'And how many Marthas live in the parish all together, I wonder?' continued Cheryl. 'How many caring non-Christians, I mean.'

'I don't know,' I said truthfully. 'I don't know how many people live in the parish.'

'Well, perhaps you should,' said Cheryl.

'Well I'm sure that *someone* knows,' I said defensively. 'I'm sure Canon George would be able to tell me if I asked him. Anyway, why does it matter?'

'Why does it matter?' Cheryl pulled one of her condescending faces at me. 'I would have thought that was obvious. Can you imagine any other market that you are involved in — be it pizzas or washing powder — where you would not know how many potential customers you had?'

I pulled a face back at her and finished my toast before replying.

'We're not talking about a market *here*, darling.'

She pulled another face back at me, believing that I was using the term of endearment in a patronizing way.

'Not a *market*! Well, what pray is it then?'

I stirred my coffee meaningfully, not sure what to say.

'That sort of language just isn't relevant in this case,' I said at last, aware that it was something of a lame response.

'I don't believe you sometimes!' Cheryl said in her most exasperated tone. 'If "market" is a good enough word to describe people when you're trying to get across a message about pizza toppings or added freshness in a washing powder, why isn't it a good enough word when you're trying to get across a message about God? So, it's a different message. But the people are the same.'

'Come on!' I said imploringly, trying to sound confident. Amy looked up at me from under her eyebrows. She knew when her father was on the back foot.

'The messages we're trying to put across on pizzas and washing powders are meant to get people to try them, and then stick with them in a competitive situation where there are lots of other pizzas and washing powders on offer.'

'And that's different to the kind of message the church has?'

Even *I* knew when I was digging myself a hole. I tried to change tack

'Look,' I said reasonably, 'mention marketing in church circles and you conjure up pictures of American tele-evangelists.'

'Michael,' responded Cheryl patiently, 'I'm not asking you to stick plastic daffodils on the hymn books or offer people Green Shield Stamps for coming to church. I'm talking about knowing the consumer. But *you* should be telling *me* this. I mean, what's the point?'

There was a pause. I accepted a small piece of the chocolate egg that Amy was breaking up.

'What's *what* point?' I said, confused.

'What's the point of having a clergyman who is a director of an advertising agency if he doesn't use his marketing skills to get the message across? Perhaps that's where you're going wrong.'

This was my chance. I looked hurt at the suggestion that I might be going wrong, and therefore won back the sympathy vote. Cheryl immediately realized both what she had said, and how I was using it. She laughed, adding:

'This time you know what I mean. I don't mean you're doing it, being it — any of it — wrong. But perhaps . . .'

'Yes?' I said, prompting her and wanting to hear what she had to say.

'Perhaps you ought to try less hard to be an advertising man who is trying to be a clergyman.'

'And more to be . . .?'

'More to be an advertising man with a message, a brand, a campaign, a story about God.'

I made some effort to stop Amy eating the whole of her egg as her breakfast, and Cheryl asked me if I would like some more coffee.

'I'd love some,' I said. 'But go on. Say a bit more. I've not head you put it in quite this way before.'

Cheryl sighed, pushed back her hair once again and sat down at the table.

'To be honest I'm not sure that I knew this until I said it. No, that's not true. It's been there a bit for quite a while. But it's not the sort of thing you want to hear, is it? When you're struggling to come to terms with a new way of life, you're entitled to expect support from your nearest and dearest.'

'I've never doubted your support,' I said.

'Shut up. I'm talking, remember? Now where was I?'

'Support from nearest and dearest,' I suggested.

'You've wanted to be accepted as a parish clergyman,' she continued, ignoring me, 'and so you've invested a lot of time in learning the ropes, as it were, of parish life. But I'm still not sure that it's parish life that needs you most. I think you should be *being* whatever it is God wants you to be — not with six months' authority as a parish clergyman, but with ten *years'* authority as an advertising and marketing specialist. That's it. I've said my piece. It's far too early in the morning for me to have to think this clearly, so I'm going to stop while I'm ahead. Anyway, look at the time. I'd better go and smarten myself up for church, otherwise the parish worthies will never speak to me again. And as for you, Amy Dunn, if you're sick all over your new dress, it'll be your own fault!'

* * *

The three of us travelled to St Mary's together for the main Easter Morning service which began at half past nine. Amy looked sweetness itself in a new floral dress and with a large bow in her hair. Cheryl was wearing red leggings, black boots, a leather jacket, more make-up than usual, and a large black felt hat.

'Let them pick the bones out of that!' she had said as she climbed into the car next to me.

Leaving Cheryl and Amy to take their places in the church, I made my way to the vestry to robe for the service. At half past nine on the dot, Canon George strode out to the middle of the church and shouted:

'Alleluia! Christ is risen!'

To which everyone responded:

'He is risen indeed. Alleluia!'

This happened three times, getting louder on each occasion, and at the end of all this shouting, Malcolm struck up with the opening chords of the hymn 'Jesus Christ is risen today' as the full procession entered from the side chapel.

By the time the hymn had finished, we were all in our places. I was standing beside Canon George as he began:

'The Lord be with you.'

It was then that we first heard something. A dull knocking at first. As if it might have been coming from outside the church building. Canon George must have heard it, but gamely continued, leading the congregation into the next prayer. But when we had finished the prayer, the knocking sound was still there. Only more insistent, and seemingly nearer. A regular thump, thump, thump, from somewhere near the back of the church.

Finally Canon George had to acknowledge defeat. He stopped me just as I was about to begin the invitation to the general confession, and called out to the congregation.

'I'm sorry, everyone,' he boomed through his

radio microphone. 'Frank, do you know what that noise is? Is it us, and should we be worried about it?'

There was general laughter as everyone turned towards the back of the church. Frank Foster was out of his pew, walking up and down and listening. There was a lull in the noise. We all waited expectantly. And then, sure enough, it started again. A regular thudding noise. Thump, thump, thump.

'It's coming from below here, I think,' said Frank at last. He was standing on the trap door at the back of the church. The trap door that led down to the crypt.

There was nothing for it but to bring the service to a halt until we could work out what was going on. Canon George made some announcement to this effect and asked me to help Frank. I took off my stole, and made my way down to the back of the church where by now several able-bodied men had taken it upon themselves to assemble around the trap door.

Who could tell what might be lurking there? That was the thought that I could see was in all their minds. Yet as I smiled at them supportively, I couldn't help thinking that I knew what lay below the hatch.

'OK, chaps,' said Frank. 'Stand clear. Let's get this thing open.'

Frank undid the lock and slid back the bolt. Conscious of looking somewhat out of context in my long off-white cassock-alb, I leaned forward gingerly and pulled the door open. As I did so everyone who was standing around it took a step back. For at that very moment a weather-beaten and tousled head popped up like a jack-in-the-box from the darkness below.

'Well, what are you all staring at?' said the head. 'Is this Easter Day or not?'

I looked at Frank and Frank looked at me, neither of us knowing quite what to say.

'Are you going to help me up or not?' said Josh MacDonald, for the head belonged to none other than the vagrant that I had met two days before in the churchyard. I stepped forward again and grasped the blackened hand that was being thrust in my direction.

With much grunting and groaning, Josh levered his body up and out of the crypt so that he was finally standing in the nave surrounded by the group of worshippers who had come to help. I looked at the grubby mark that Josh had deposited on my vestments as he had climbed out of the pit. Josh noticed my look of irritation and, tongue in cheek, issued a grave warning to the others.

'That's right. Don't touch me. You don't know where I've been!'

Frank decided to take charge. Whilst he felt it would not be appropriate to dragoon the interloper forcibly from the church, he suspected that the service could only really begin again once the initiator of the disturbance had been removed from the scene. He began in diplomatic vein.

'Right, my friend. After being cooped up down there, I think you'd better get outside and take some fresh air, don't you?'

Josh looked askance at him.

'Friend? Do you call me "friend"? Well, perhaps I am. Who knows? I am, after all, risen. And it is, after all, Easter Day. Is it not? Who knows? Perhaps I am your Christ, come again. Then indeed would I be your friend. But if not he, then perhaps not your friend. As I say, "Who knows?"'

Josh's words had an immediate effect on the assembled people. Where before everyone had been either amused or bemused by the strange scene, those feelings were replaced by ones of indignity, offence or disappointment at what had been said.

'There, now,' said Frank, overcoming his concerns about touching the man, and taking him by the elbow. 'That's enough of that sort of talk. Let's go outside, shall we? And then you can tell me all about yourself and how you came to be down there. In the crypt.'

I felt Canon George arrive at my side.

'Why, it's you!' he gasped, looking directly at Josh. 'What on earth . . .?'

'Or in heaven, eh, Vicar?' said Josh. 'There are

stranger things, Horatio. Who knows? Perhaps I'm one of them. One of those strange things. Eh?'

'Perhaps you are, my friend,' persisted Frank. 'Come along. These good people are trying to get on with their service. And you're disturbing them.'

'Disturbing them?' said Josh. 'I bet I am. I should think it must be *very* disturbing to have a man come up out of a tomb on Easter Day after he's been there for . . . How long? Three days? Was it Good Friday when I crept down into your dark hole? And here I am, safe and well. Hmm. Something to think about, eh, Vicar?'

Frank was coughing and urging his case.

'All right, Mr Official Church Person. I'm going,' said Josh, with more of a hint of sadness than anger in his voice. 'But tell me this, Vicar?' he said, turning once more to face Canon George. 'How will you know when *he* comes again? How will you *know* him? If you're so sure it's not me, how will you be sure when you're looking at *him*, right in the eye? And how are you going to explain all this?'

He flung open his arms to indicate the whole of the church building and all the people in it, and he threw back his head in laughter. At this Frank was ready to become more directive, but Josh had anticipated this and was already pushing past the ring of onlookers towards the door.

'No, don't bother following me,' he called out. 'You won't want to follow where *I'm* going. And as I'm a good-hearted sort of bloke I won't be taking this up with the authorities. The fact that one of you locked me up against my will. It's all right. Mum's the word. I'll keep it very quiet. And, don't worry, I won't be back!'

As he left, he waved at everyone, and as he disappeared out through the main door we could hear him calling back:

'Happy Easter, Christians! Happy Easter!'

Frank made a move to follow him, but Canon George edged forward and stayed him with his hand.

'No, Frank. Not now. Not now.'

Frank shrugged his shoulders, and bent down to replace and lock the trap door.

Canon George and I made our way back to the front of the church in as dignified a manner as we could. As we walked I whispered in his ear that I thought Josh must have been sleeping somewhere in the church on Good Friday afternoon and then slipped down into the crypt whilst we were unloading the cross from the top of the car. I could only suppose that a combination of tiredness and possibly drunkenness had meant that Josh had slept down there for more than a day. Canon George looked troubled. But he put a brace face on it. Switching his microphone back on he said:

'I apologize for that interruption. The person whom you just saw emerging from the crypt is a gentleman of the road who has been living rough nearby for a few days. I regret to say that he must have gone into the crypt unnoticed when it was open, and been locked in. I can only give thanks that we were here to notice his banging this morning. I don't think any of us would like to contemplate what might have happened had we not heard him.'

He looked around at the congregation and smiled broadly.

'Can I suggest a very short pause so that we may

compose our thoughts before we resume our normal service?'

There was much nodding of heads, and I was grateful for the chance to slip out to wash my hands and reposition my stole before taking up my position in the sanctuary once more.

Five minutes later, and probably no more than about fifteen minutes after the knocking was first heard, we were all back in our usual places ready to worship God in our usual way. Canon George gave me the nod, and I began where we had left off.

'Let us confess our sins.'

* * *

Cheryl, Amy and I only arrived home at noon. The strange goings-on at the service had quite naturally caused a great deal of talk over coffee afterwards, and I found myself buttonholed by one parishioner after another wanting to hear what little I knew about the story of Josh MacDonald. There was not much to be said, and yet I suspected that by the end of the morning Chinese whispers would have ensured for Josh a special place in the folklore of St Mary's.

By the time we arrived home some of the early and sparkling excitement of the morning and the birth of Maria's baby had been rounded by a feeling of weariness and escape. With celebration, however, still a clear priority, I went straight to the fridge to liberate the bottle of champagne that would mark the end of our Lent abstinence, and the coming of Easter.

I poured two large glasses, and one small one for my daughter, who would not be denied a drop of what she laughingly called the fizzy-wizzy.

Passing the drinks to Cheryl and Amy, I held my glass up to the sunlight that was sloping through the window in long, bright shafts. As the bubbles rose to the surface in endless agitation, I felt the past weeks flowing through me and out into the white hot stream of dust-bearing light. The ordination, the services, the meetings, the people, the mistakes, the hopes, the love, and the questions.

'Here's to our first six months as a clergy family,' I said, clinking glasses with the two favourite women in my life and feeling the tears once more welling up behind my eyes.

'Here's to our new life,' said Cheryl, clinking again. 'May it always be new.'

Amy clinked glasses for a third time, smiled a smile of innocent joy and said, 'Happy Easter everyone!'

THE END
(or perhaps the beginning)